THE UNIVERSE OF SCIENCE

LIST OF VOLUMES PUBLISHED IN THIS SERIES

Each bound in clothette, 1s. net.

The Thinker's Library, No. 67.

THE UNIVERSE OF SCIENCE

BY

H. LEVY

Professor of Mathematics at the Imperial College of Science,
University of London

REVISED AND EXPANDED

LONDON:

WATTS & CO.,

5 & 6 JOHNSON'S COURT, FLEET STREET, E.C. 4

First Published 1932
First Published in the Thinker's Library (revised) 1938

Printed and Published in Great Britain by C. A. Watts & Co. Limited,
5 & 6 Johnson's Court, Fleet Street, London, E.C. 4.

INTRODUCTION

SINCE the period of the Great War social, industrial, and intellectual life on all continents has been marked by ever-increasing instability and insecurity. Outwardly Science has placed in the hands of man weapons of power and control which, if wielded intelligently, could banish human misery and inaugurate a reign of material and cultural prosperity unprecedented in his history. It is apparently not to be. The scientific movement, the child of civilised society itself, has made demands for communal adjustment that its slow-moving parent has been unable to meet, and a period of re-valuation, material and intellectual, is inevitable.

A society can remain stable only when its relative parts are geared to change at comparable speeds. Science, the driving power, has developed at its own pace without the evolution of a corporate conception of steady adjustment between the static and dynamic features of society as a whole. Communities are not self-contained eternal, economic entities divided off by political frontiers. The scientific exposure of the mineral resources of the globe, scattered broadcast by Nature's bountiful hand, irrespective of the national barriers that man has established in his past struggles to survive, and coupled with the international and inter-racial validity of all scientific knowledge, has stripped these boundaries of everything but an historical significance. Man has inherited the Earth and the goodness thereof, and not merely political and temporary elements of it. So much at any rate Science has taught him. His struggles and travails will continue until he has learnt sufficient wisdom to come to terms with the demands of Nature.

These, in a sense, are the external aspects of the scientific revolution. Within the body of scientific knowledge there have been internal repercussions. The theoretical discoveries in Relativity, Quantum Theory and in Atomic Physics generally have brought to light problems of fundamental significance to our intellectual understanding of the world we live in, and its meaning to us on the ethical, simple and æsthetic planes. The age of materialism, that reached its zenith during last century, is giving place to a new synthesis. The interpreters of the new knowledge and understanding, Sir James Jeans, Sir Arthur Eddington, Professor Millikan, General Smuts, to mention only a few, have almost without exception approached their problems against a background of outworn Idealist Philosophy none the less significant in its colouring because it has been unobtrusively though tacitly present. The pendulum has swung in the opposite direction. It is a reaction against the materialism of a past generation, as mechanical and as uncritical as was its religious counterpart. A new approach to materialism is called for.

If the meaning of the newer knowledge is to be adequately assessed, it can be done only by the fullest recognition of the lessons of history. Science is primarily a movement, a social outgrowth serving social ends, and all attempts to isolate any aspect of it, be it even the purest mathematics, from the social movement of which it is an integral part, can lead to nothing but false and dangerous conclusions.

The assertion of contemporary scientists, who state that the Universe is a fickle collection of indeterminate happenings, and a great thought in the Mind of its Architect, a Pure Mathematician, serves merely to divert the activity of the scientific brain from its concentration on the contradictions and confusions of the all too real outward world to a state of passive and unreal contemplation.

In the laboratory of Science as in the battlefield of Society, speculations and theories emerge from, and must be tested by, actual participation in the work. Only the theory of practice can survive. Speculation divorced from the needs of man, in the sense that it cannot be put to the test of action, remains mere isolated word spinning, a pleasant game for theorists, but if indulged in at a period of critical change a dangerous and reactionary game.

Man runs off easily along the tangent of speculation, isolating subjects and objects from their context, and building up elaborate structures on these isolated paths. From the changing matrix of the universe we separate out its biological, its chemical, its historical features. Our schools and our universities are designed to accentuate the isolation. Already at the school stage, and most certainly at the stages of higher education, experts in these " subjects " deal with their fields as if these existed by themselves, and as if their full significance could be derived from an internal study of these matters. So deep-rooted has specialist study become that the primary subject, what might perhaps be called Social Culture, of which these are mere subsidiary aspects, nowhere finds a place. The raw student emerging already highly specialised from school life, enters on the next stage of his career to submit to still more intensive specialisation. As a teacher he returns to school life to carry the process a stage further. From a generation or two of this kind of practice there naturally emerges an elaborate philosophical justification embodied in such phrases as "Science for its own sake," as if the pursuit of anything could be a complete end in itself.

Values are dangerous matters in which to dabble, mainly because there can be no absolute criterion against which they may be assessed. We all apparently possess our own individual scale of values, bound up socially with the material and mental exercises we enjoy. Within a movement such as Science, separated into its almost watertight compartments of Mathematics, Physics, Chemistry, Biology, Psychology, Engineering, etc., the values that are attached to individual developments bear little relation to the wider movement. Each group pursues its way along its own tangent, setting up its own criteria of importance. In an environment where the danger is ever present that only those fields of study may be permitted or encouraged that bear an immediate relation to the industrial practice of the day, this acts as a distinct safeguard, but it inevitably builds up systems of values in each subject that cannot be reconciled as between subjects. That reconciliation will be effected only when scientists recognise the social roots and the social function of their movement. There is no organised body that represents them in this respect.

In this book I have endeavoured to sketch in broad outline the background against which the scientific movement has to be seen. By recognising it as a feature of a developing society, we can assess the methods it has evolved to select those aspects of the changing world that are amenable to scientific analysis, the nature of the tools and instruments it has found essential in handling them, and the criteria of scientific truth. The same process shows up in relief the field within which science can at present operate with assurance, and exposes to view the tendencious idealism of contemporary expositors for many of whose pronouncements science provides no justification whatsoever. The mathematician, in particular, has become so dominant of recent years, and the field of experimental science has become so impregnated with his terminology, that Mathematical Physics, to many interpreters, has taken on the appearance almost of a separate science where facts about the world are *proved* rather than discovered by observation and experiment. As the treatment becomes more and more abstract, the symbols become the realities, and their properties when capable of being re-interpreted become evidence to these writers that there is a new mystery in the Universe. The Numbers, that initially were mere measures of qualities, are divorced from their setting, and Science usurped by Mathematics is represented as dealing only with superficial structure, and so the Universe itself eludes us. So much of scientific advance, however (and the confusion of its interpreters), depends on the symbolic nature of Mathematics, and the capacity it provides for concise expression, that I have included a chapter on Mathematics written as I hope sufficiently simply to be followed by anyone unfamiliar with the subject, and yet carrying it forward far enough to enable one to appreciate how mathematical methods are used as an instrument in scientific discovery. The succeeding chapter on the scope of scientific prediction, with its discussion of Determinism and Free Will, can be followed even by those for whom the discipline of Chapter III may be too severe. The general standpoint adopted will, I think, be most clearly seen in Chapters I and II, particularly in the latter where, what I have called the Method of Isolation, is expounded. I make no apology for the apparently new use of the words Isolation and Isolate, where philosophers have probably used Abstraction or Exclusion. These latter terms have other connotations that would be objectionable in the present context. Apart from this, the word isolation is already in use in various branches of science in a sense not different from that in which I have used it here. I have merely given it a wider significance.

CONTENTS

CHAPTER I

THE CHANGING PATTERN

§ 1.

THE case presented in this book is not likely to survive criticism in every detail. There never was and there never can be such a case. The world is not a mosaic of simple events, a geometrical pattern that can be completely pieced together until there is not a crack or a seam visible; nor is it a self-contained completely accessible mechanism easily broken down into parts and just as easily assembled at will. Common sense sees the world rather as an enormous inter-related dynamic muddle with intermittent patches of order and sanity. Answers cannot immediately be found to every question that can be asked, nor can we always tell whether such a question is sensible or not. For, as we shall see, the problem of asking sensible questions is no child's pastime. It requires a special technique. It has taken many generations even to recognise that the frame of a question may determine the kind of picture that will be inserted.

Who would care to assert that a few years hence he will be found still clinging to the attitude he adopts now ? A few years ago he probably held a different view, and held it equally firmly. In retrospect we can see that the tenacity of our beliefs is no measure of their accuracy. One has little to do with the other, but the fact that we have come to change our outlook is a good sign. Whether it be regarded as progress or the reverse, however, what is inescapable is that beliefs can almost be dated. They are events in our history, they are our landmarks. You can look back on that succession of finger-posts and recognise the *being* that was you gradually being transformed, and culminating in the being that is you now. You cannot dissociate yourself from them even if you wished, for they are part of yourself, an historically changing object. Friends come and go, and leave their trace. Ideas enlarge and are purified as they pass through the fire of experience. The intimate tender friendships of youth pass into the sober intellectual acquaintanceships of middle age. Youthful enthusiasms elude us after the first yellowing signs of cynicism. Slowly and almost imperceptibly we unfold under the gathering pressure of a world immanent with new experience. We are not merely the changing beings we now are, the present stage of us. We are the whole of our historically conscious life.

Nor are we the isolated thread of personal experience we are inclined to picture. Every element of that thread has been woven into the texture of some cloth, it has passed in and out of a succession of environments from which we at that stage could not be disentangled. The internal reflection of ourselves is for ever balanced by an external picture of the object slowly changing from boyhood, struggling through youthfulness to manhood, in the successive settings in which these periods were passed. Each of us has inherited a social environment, home, school, friends and acquaintances, science, music, literature, churches, prisons, Trade Unions, works and professions, societies, and Laws. We find these institutions ready for us, formed and set by generations of established tradition and yet changing. From the moment we draw in our first breath, these, formative and conditioning, exert their influence upon us, circumscribing our behaviour in countless subtleties, colouring our thoughts to ourselves, to our fellow-men, and to the material forces we encounter. Indeed, to say we have inherited this powerful and firmly established piece of social machinery is to give a false emphasis. *It has inherited us.* We are delivered up to it at birth, and it moulds us and shapes us. To an extent we fear to realise, we are its creatures. We have its taboos, its religions, its politics, its language. It has words we cannot utter, thoughts we must not think, criticisms we dare not voice, and organs of the body we examine only in private. It has habits and decencies, cruelties and crudities, we assimilate so naturally as to be unaware of them. If they are pointed out to us we cannot, we dare not, see them. Even in these respects it is not uniform. It has its classes and its masses, each with its own customs, its rights, its taboos, and its tacit assumptions. It has its class distinctions, class habits, and its class cultures. Embedded in this communal structure are historical relics of our savage ancestry sometimes scarcely disguised. Birth, marriage, death, religion, each bears its historical rites.

How close we are to the primitive man we, of the scientific age, have hardly begun to realise. Scarcely ten thousand generations separate us from the early savage. As you sit here reading you can imagine your ancestral file stretching outwards in a long historical line, unconscious of itself, father, grandfather, and their parents in succession. Only your immediate neighbours are aware of the very existence of the procession itself, and what its significance is they can scarcely guess. A few hundred yards away a primitive agriculture is just emerging, and long before the procession has reached the outskirts of this city its members are scarcely distinguishable from wandering savages. A few more miles of this line of beings—my family, or yours—and to all appearances they are mere ape-like animals with no trace of the civilisation of which we are so proud. That begins almost within earshot. In the passage outside, with animal ferocity they are busy burning witches, and yet someone is suggesting to his incredulous hearers that the way to discover how the world works is to experiment with it, to toy with it, as it experiments with us and toys with us. About us, our friends, these modern cultured people, have hardly recovered from a world-wide slaughter and starvation of men, women, and children. In an age outstepped by its limited scientific knowledge they can only gape in superstitious surprise at the mysterious disease that condemns whole classes of society to perpetual penury. They invent their justifications and their explanations just as glibly as they demonstrated the ethical need for international murder. They too are a mere episode in history, a passing phase, but to themselves they are the climax, the consummation of knowledge and experience, and whatsoever surpasses the scope of their understanding is mysterious. Personal ailments and mental aberrations, dreams, premonitions, trade depressions and unemployment, colour bars and racial antipathies, personal and religious experiences—they are to them an unexplored universe of caprice and mystery.

These, then, are man's historic bonds from which he can no more shake himself loose than you or I can disentangle ourselves from our own individual past histories. We are elements of it, while its prejudices, its traditions, its falsehoods, and its brutalities reflect themselves in our behaviour in the face of the new problems that always confront us. At each successive stage in history we are apt to regard our explanations, our religions, our philosophies, and our logic, as individual and complete, ignorant of the fact that each one of us largely mirrors the ideas and beliefs of our own particular epoch in this historic pageant. Nor does the scale of history alone lay out the whole field within which humanity moves. It is but one base-line. There is no history without geography, no Time without Space, for the history of a race or of a nation is profoundly affected by its place on the surface of the globe. Neither can be isolated one from the other. Emerging from the mud and slime of the past man has found himself restricted to a thin atmospheric layer that surrounds his world, relatively as thin as a coat of varnish. Within this narrow band he crawls and gropes, trying this and that, peeping here and there, and from this restricted experience working out his view of the universe. Gregariously he settles in patches, forming economically isolated groups. The geographical setting primarily delimits the lines of the social structure he erects with its institutions and its history. Pasture lands and fertile soils, rocky coasts and fishing-beds, mineral deposits and wooded country, each contributes its peculiar form of society, and gradually, with the evolution of tools and machines, scientific instruments, transport on sea, land, and air, telegraphs, telephones, and wireless, under the gathering stress of human needs the economic isolation of communities becomes unstable, and breaks down, and the clash occurs between conflicting social and industrial group interests. The inertia of traditional institutions established within a restricted geographical area with their roots in the form of society, in the forms of production and of distribution that have there evolved and become set, renders them incapable of easy adjustment to the rapidly enlarging environment. Man has inherited the Earth, not merely isolated elements thereof. Conflicts on the material plane are reflected by con-

tradictory philosophies on the intellectual plane, and
wider problems begin to emerge.

The child of the slums sees the world as an end-
less vista of bricks and hovels, or, if he has strayed
beyond the frontiers in action and in thought, as a
vicious contrast between wealth and want. To
the factory hand the world is a vast workshop of
belts and pulleys, a world of humming production,
and he a cog in its mechanism. To the tradesman
we are a nation of housewives. The universe of
the financier revolves around the Stock Exchange.
Nations are built on the economic resources of the
country in which they dwell, and individuals reflect
the atmosphere in which they live and earn their
livelihood. We are creatures of our historical and
our geographical environment. We are sailors tied
to our ship, long since habituated to the smell
of salt water.

So, when we state that this view or that
view is an exact picture of the world of reality, we
shall have missed the first lesson of history and of
geography if we imagine that it is the last word.
There is no last word, no matter how certain or
sacred it may appear. Every explanation must be
examined in its historical setting, in its environment
in time and space. It is never final. This new-
found ability to see ourselves in a space-time

perspective, to see ourselves as a permanent and inevitable link in this chain of ancestors, to recognise ourselves as the creatures of the social environment that has inherited us, and the social structure so much determined by the hard facts of geography, is perhaps the most significant change that has been brought about by the science of the last century.

§ 2.

There are those who would assert that these are shifting sands on which to base a view of life; that man cannot live without solid ground beneath his feet, that only by initially accepting permanent, unchanging principles can the world about us be understood, and that anything less than the Absolute is unsatisfying. It is probably true to say that man has always sought permanence. It has been the *motif* of a great deal that is scientific. The search for certainty in experimental work is little more than the search for things and states permanent. In the past, science has attempted to set up unchanging laws. It strives to make predictions as if there existed underlying principles of a permanent nature. In its day, science has established many such absolutes, Laws of Conservation, as they have been called. . . . The Conservation of Matter,

of Momentum, of Energy . . . and principles also
. . . the Principle of Least Action, the Principle of
Least Work. Fortunately, with all its principles,
its theories, and its laws, science has to work its
way through a very fine mesh before its absolutes
can be accepted, if at all, within the framework of
knowledge. Its gauge is the changing universe itself,
and its principles are mere tentative guiding lines.

These, however, are not the permanences that
are meant by those seeking a finality that science
cannot offer. Outside and above science there is
said to be an Absolute Purpose in the universe, and
it is the function of human endeavour to uncover it.
There is a supreme Dialectician who knows not
merely every infinitesimal detail of the universe, but
appreciates it as the interlocking, interpenetrated
whole that it is. This Absolute Unchanging Being
strives to guide us into the path of goodness or
drive us from the path of wickedness. The human
soul, in so far as it reflects the divine purpose, is
supreme over matter; man is free and master of his
destiny.

Such assertions are of a totally different order from
those of science. They are immutable, imposed from
above, and subject to no experimental criterion of
truth, for any such test would be subsidiary to it.
The backyards of science are littered with discarded

Principles, destroyed by a single fact, for the world of science, like the world of reality, is in a perpetual state of renewal. Therein lies its strength, for it is geared to that real world. A structure of absolute moral and religious beliefs erected initially as beyond criticism, imposed upon a changing society from above rather than emerging from below, has no affinity with science, whatever personal solace and comfort it may provide, for it assumes that the facts of life, including the material facts of the world, can be compassed within a rigidly prescribed framework. It has taken several centuries of history for the scientific movement to be emancipated from just these cramping human assumptions. The writings of many scientists show, alas, that the emancipation has not yet been completed.

The scientific movement, like the individual scientist, cannot dissociate itself completely from its past. It is itself a manifestation of social life. It springs from and flourishes in a developing society, and its strength resides in the fact that it is so rooted. It is not simply the sum total of scientists at any given moment. All the statements of every accredited scientist are not necessarily accepted within the body of scientific knowledge. It has its criteria of what is suitable and what is not suitable of acceptance, and these have grown along with its history. It is an experienced movement that can look back with cynical amusement on the uncritical enthusiasms of its youth. It remembers its philosopher's stones, its electric fluids, its phlogiston, and its ethers. It has learnt to tread warily and with caution, but as a movement it has not yet learnt to speak. It gazes in mere puzzled silence at individual scientists who step in blindly where the movement would not tread. But no individual can be the spokesman of a movement. Each is a mirror that reflects, however imperfectly, the movement of which he is a part, but the image is coloured and distorted by his own experience and his own history, from which he cannot disentangle himself. The movement transcends the man. He imposes his private and personal prejudices upon it at the risk of his own confusion. Only a genius sensing its group needs contributes to it precisely what it requires.

To each of us our life has been a chapter in our history, and is a portion, a tiny portion, of the history of the community. When, however, the final tomes are written, the personal experiences of you and me will not appear, but, in so far as we are mentioned at all, therein will be shown how the changing universe, its processes, and its movements into which we drifted were reflected in us. In bold outline it will sketch not any personal experience of the world as expressed by the individual, but the manner in which the changing pattern of the universe has penetrated into that person's consciousness of it. The universe and its history cannot be regarded as composed entirely either of my experiences of it, or of *our* experiences, if such a summation has any significance. That is not the prime stuff. These are resultant effects. You are not a complete and organised whole that sees the world from some Olympian height unruffled by the swirling storm in the valleys below. On the contrary, you are part of that medley, buffeted hither and thither by every creature and every force you encounter. You have your history, your consciousness, from which you cannot shake yourself loose, just as every particle of air has its story to tell. Your history is that of a man among men of your profession, a history of a man among the larger currents we call movements, and these movements are a feature of the larger movement we call social development. There is nothing that can be shaken free of its environment, neither the straw in the eddy nor the current between its banks. A scientific worker can no more dissociate himself from the effect the scientific movement has had upon him than the scientific movement can divorce itself from the social

environment out of which it has become differentiated as a recognisable socially important factor.
The scientific worker is a tiny pointer in science, just
as science is a pointer in communal life. Nevertheless, we seem to study the world about us as if we
were self-contained entities, completely isolated from
everything else. There, outside us, are trees,
houses, animals, and human beings. We detect
events taking place in that external world, individuals in conversation, animals in motion, machinery
humming, flowers giving forth scent; they seem
to have no relation, no connection, with us at
all. We are each completely external to them.
We are in a privileged position, the unbiased
observer studying movement and behaviour. Each
of us, apparently, sees a wholly objective universe
quite unrelated to us except that, in some unaccount-
able way, we are interested in its problems. Presently each will produce his solution and everything
will fit together perfectly. We shall play no part
in the explanation, for we are each the dispassionate
observer.

The apparent objectivity of this outlook is
fallacious. Are we so distinct and self-contained
as this attitude would suggest? The suspicion that
our thoughts and our estimates are coloured by the
environments through which we have passed during

our life-times has already begun to dawn on us. Even our bodies are not the unique objects we imagine. They can be broken up into a mere collection of constantly changing particles, portions of the sea, the air, the clouds, and the materials under the earth. Atoms that were once parts of your body may now be contained in mine, or in that of some animal in a distant part of the globe. In that sense we are all omnivorous animals. If modern physical astronomy is correct in its theories regarding the history of the solar system, we can trace the chemical aspect of our genealogical tree even further back. At a very remote epoch in the past it would seem that a large and swiftly moving star swung suddenly from the outer regions of space into the range of attraction of the sun, and in its passage a mass of hot gas was torn from its side. From such an accident, as it is sometimes called, was the Earth born; although, indeed, it is no more an accident than any other event in the universe. Whether accident, design, or sheer necessity, however, the materials that compose your flesh, blood, and bones were at one time many million miles away from here in the heart of the sun. Every human body is, in fact, a mottled mass of molecular history, and the blueness of its blood or the lowliness of its origin shows itself socially

rather than chemically. We are not merely inter-
nationalists, we are universalists.

We are, of course, far too parochial in all our
attitudes, and they ill become our cosmopolitan
histories. In the study we may feel among old
friends, the books we have had for years, the same
table, the same chair, even the same smell of stale
tobacco. We close our hands together suddenly
and trap within them a small mass of air, the air
of the room. What a tale could not each of these
invisible molecules tell of his wanderings within
these last few days ! this one from the Sahara, that
from the Pole, and this from the wide Atlantic. A
motley crew which within a week has wandered
freely from Jerusalem to Madagascar, a jostling,
more international crowd here within the hollow of
the palms than any to be found along the boule-
vards of the most cosmopolitan city.

§ 3.

We begin our outlook on the world about us as
if we were something physically unique, different,
and permanently separated off, and however we
turn we discover that, chemically at any rate, we
are scarcely to be distinguished from the rest of
our changing environment. A few moments' reflection, then, and we have lost our separate corporeal

identity. But if our seeming physical permanence is an illusion, if our habits of mind and body are largely imposed on us by our history and the history of the institutions through which we have passed, if they have grown and unfolded, process-like, the final result is to secure to each of us a personality, distinct and differentiated off from the rest of the universe, if only in the sense that it is a unique combination of these very factors we have exposed.

So much is true, but it is a personality within the framework of the world we inhabit, the society in which we participate, the processes of which we are constituent parts. We dare not arbitrarily isolate ourselves even in thought from the rest of the universe without indulging in vain fancies and futile imaginings. Here a separate entity one may tread the floor of the room, itself a portion of the house, an integral portion of the earth. There does not exist a separate and completely isolated entity " I." By an effort of the imagination one can suppose oneself in the outer confines of space, remote from any material part of the universe, outside Space and Time. It is a pure effort of the imagination. What we call " I " is inseparable from the moving piece of matter that will still bear our name when it has crumbled to dust. Because certain parts seem to hang together over an extended period of time a name is given to these collective parts. We do precisely the same with what we call inanimate objects in this world. Here is a cigarette: we examine it, and find it is a mass of stranded tobacco rolled up and enclosed in a cylinder of paper. This whole thing we call a cigarette; but is there such a thing as a cigarette *as such*? It rests between our fingers, on the hand, attached to the arm, part of the body, on the surface of the earth. No one has ever seen a cigarette *per se*, we have no knowledge of cigarettes *as such*. And yet of course it is very convenient indeed to take this collection of material and give it the one name, cigarette. It is convenient because in social communication with other people we wish to refer just to that restricted collection, that chip of the larger universe. But of course it is a chip, and to pretend it has an isolated existence apart from this larger and wider entity is a pure effort of the imagination. Meanwhile what has happened to the cigarette? It has changed its appearance, its length is considerably reduced. There is some ash on the end of it, and there is a diffused smoke in the atmosphere of the room. Which is the cigarette? It has changed under our eyes. It was a cigarette only five minutes ago; does the same cigarette now consist of this stump, this ash, and that smoke?

Here, however, is something different—a table, solid and unchanging; once a table always a table, one would suppose. But is that bit of the universe we call a table as continuous an object as all that? Look at the cigarette; it changed under our very eyes. If we were to examine the table by the aid of highly refined instruments, we should find that, far from the table remaining permanent and unchanged while we have been reading this, all sorts of extraordinary things have been happening to it. Little particles of it have become rubbed off, and others have adhered to it. It has given up moisture to the air or absorbed some from it. If we are really careful about what we say, it is not honestly the same table. It is a different table, very like the other, but still different, or, if it is the same table, it is a changing sameness. And so with everything else. You and I have changed considerably during the last few minutes, and yet, having had names given to us, names which persist throughout Time, we delude ourselves with the idea that there does correspond something solid and permanent which also persists throughout Time. It is, as we see, a complete fallacy. If we look back, we can see what we were. The environment of which we are an integral part, of which we are a chip, so to speak, is itself in a continuous state of flux. At no

B

two consecutive moments is there anything unchanged.

If we are to obtain a just appreciation of what
human knowledge is, it is above all essential that
we should strip ourselves initially, here and now,
of this fallacy so exposed—the fallacy of self-
isolation, the fallacy of static existence. This will
be extremely difficult, for all our habits of speech
that have grown up throughout the ages, from the
time when the first word was formulated by our
savage ancestors, are interwoven and interpenetrated by just this illusion of the permanence and
separate existence of objects in the universe. Every
noun and every personal pronoun is a trap to
suggest that our analysis is arbitrary. We must
learn to grasp this idea of the uniformity of nature,
and that the things about us, including ourselves,
to which names are to be attached, are all temporary
and changing portions of it.

§ 4.

At the risk of what may seem but vain repetition,
let us briefly consider the stage we have reached in
order to examine in what direction we are led.
The universe is our datum, it is given, it exists, it
is the everyday world of common sense and common
experience. It is a world of process. Mankind is

just such a changing feature, a component and indissoluble part of it, and yet so definitely differentiated from the whole that it is easily induced to isolate itself in thought as if it were an independent thing; and therein, as we have seen, lies a danger. Mankind, again, with its historical and its geographical aspects, is a criss-cross pattern of races, movements, and individuals, each drawing its historical thread through the larger pattern. So differentiated are individuals and their histories that each again is induced to isolate himself from the larger movements as if he were a self-contained whole, and to offer his differentiated experiences, the picture of the larger universe that has soaked through his senses to him, as *the* view of the universe. We have seen how that view may be coloured by his immediate and local surroundings, how specialised his sample of the universe may be. There are several forms of individual vanity that are thereby exposed. There is a feature called language and social intercourse that individuals employ to describe their experiences. This language has a history and is a social datum. Embedded in it are tacit assumptions that may unwittingly give rise to false explanations. They are relics of a past of more limited experience. We have to recognise their dangers and deficiencies. Again, individuals exhibit what we have called imagination. As yet we know little of this activity, but one of its functions is to recognise processes in isolating them. It is a powerful but sometimes dangerous weapon, as we shall presently perceive. By its means man can regard himself as isolated from the rest of the universe, and view the world as an objective entity dissociated from himself as if he were entirely outside. This is false; he is completely inside it; he may not be much of it, but he is part of it. There is another form of vanity that hinders us. Accustomed as individuals to acquire their appreciation of the universe through their individual senses, there are those who suggest that the whole universe is a mere figment of their own imagination. It has no existence apart from themselves. They are the people, and the universe will die with them. To the extreme objectivist the individual is entirely outside the universe. To the extreme idealist the universe is entirely inside himself. In reality, we are entirely inside the universe, and *the problem for us is to find an answer to the question, How do the world processes percolate down to individuals?* The universe is the subject of the verb " to exist," not a static, but a dynamic essence. Its being is, therefore, not in question, but, as we have seen, our interpretation of its processes may be vitiated in innumerable ways.

There are certain criticisms that immediately spring to the mind. I have thrown doubt on the adequacy of language as a means of exposing the workings of nature, and yet I have laid down the broad basis of the whole position in terms of the very language whose weakness I have exposed. There is no answer to that criticism except that it is the best that can be done. Mankind is working its way out of a morass, and there is no clear starting-point. It is some comfort to remember that, after all, language is a tool, an instrument, and the history of tools suggests at least that it is not impossible by means of a blunt tool to produce a sharper one, and ultimately an instrument of very great precision. For the flint axes of the Stone Age were the actual forerunners of the most delicate scientific apparatus of to-day. We have passed from rough-hewn stones to surfaces flat to within one millionth of an inch. As the experience of the race widens, so new distinctions are forced upon us, and invalid distinctions are swept away. Old words with their false implications become obsolete, and their place is taken by new and more precise ones. Tools and instruments are weapons of discovery themselves, and as such gradually serve to carve out the very language itself. The history of technology implies the history of a language of increasing precision.

Is the kind of man here sketched, with his fears, his bias, his false traditions, his proximity to the animal, a being on whose judgment and understanding it is possible to rely for a picture of the universe? It will be warped and distorted, it will be unstable, it will change with time, it will be insecure, it will be false. This is unfortunately the case, but again it is the best we can do. It is, after all, man's picture of a universe, but it is a universe which he cannot escape. In his explanations he has only two directions in which he can turn. He can turn to his imaginations, his fears, and his primitive terrors, and these, as we shall see, are dangerous and insecure supports upon which to rest. But willy-nilly he must also turn directly to the universe of which he is a part, and base his explanations on what is imposed upon him there. That at any rate can serve him as a check, a testing ground, an anchor that prevents him from drifting too far afield. It is all very tentative, very uncertain, but it is well that man should recognise just how his hands are tied.

Whence comes this knowledge of the universe, even of its existence, but from man and his senses? Has he not experienced it all, and reconstructed it into a logical and consistent whole? Does the picture of the universe, then, not emerge in reality from his own inner consciousness in the first instance, and therefore is it not clear that the path to understanding commences at the source of personal knowledge, the awareness, the consciousness of the human being, and leads outwards from there? Surely the human mind is the source of all our knowledge from which all explanations flow. Surely nothing is known about the universe except such facts as have passed through the medium of the human mind. Is not Mind, then, the fundamental stuff of existence? This is what the idealist asserts. He would build the universe upon the individual mind.

There are two principal forms of idealism about which it is desirable to say a few words, since we shall continually encounter such views in the writings of many scientific interpreters. There is, in the first place, Subjective Idealism. This asserts that the individual is aware only of the activities of his senses, his sense data, what is given to his mind by his senses, and of no reality beyond these. The seeming objectivity of the world is then merely a construct, a piecing together of these promptings of his senses. This attitude has been referred to already as a species of human vanity, but of course that does not dismiss it. We, who commence at the opposite end of the scale, can recognise that here is an individual reacting to the universe in which man is, but, by an effort of the imagination, separating himself off mentally from it. In his thought he is the creator of the greatest works of genius and the most blatant follies of mankind. Has he not constructed them all in his own mind? If there still exists anyone who actually adheres to this theory and follows it, he has isolated himself from the rest of humanity. It is a brave gesture, but it is the supreme futility. In practice there are no subjective idealists of this type. Even Bishop Berkeley was driven to postulate a God, an objective external entity, in order that he himself might exist as a thought in His mind.

Idealism of this type is not in fact encountered explicitly in the interpretations of modern science, but it shows itself in other ways. It shows itself in the manner in which scientists and laymen alike frequently assume that what is cogent and inescapable to their minds *must* correspond to an inevitable state of affairs in the physical world. The world processes must proceed and must have proceeded according to their logical scheme, as if this consisted of a set of absolute propositions which the mind could set down for all time. This view is the elevation *a priori* of what appears as a mental and logical necessity, above experimental evidence. " As we trace the stream of Time backwards," says Sir James Jeans in *The Mysterious Universe*, " we encounter many indications that, after a long enough journey, we *must* come to its source, a time before which the present universe did not exist. Nature frowns upon perpetual-motion machines, and it is *a priori* very unlikely that her universe will provide an example on the grand scale of the mechanism she abhors "; and again : " It [Entropy] is still increasing rapidly, and so *must* have had a beginning; there *must* have been what we may describe as a ' creation ' at a time not infinitely remote " (*The Mysterious Universe*, p. 144).

Sir James Jeans is not here concerned with directly ascertainable evidence, for he discusses events prior to an epoch of possible observation. He takes the evidence he has *now* regarding the physical and mechanical laws of operation. He takes his brain and his rational necessities *now* as a static picture, as he has emerged biologically and socially, and he tells us what his " must " is. Having thus stated something about his state of mind *now*, we are left to infer that it is evidence for a past act of creation. He has indulged a purely mental exercise on matters outside the range of possible physical verification; it is a thoroughly unscientific prediction —incapabl of being checked, directly or indirectly.

Here we see the belief expressed that the human mind stands above the mere requirements of the physical world, that its reasoning and its logical proofs are sufficient in themselves to ensure that its findings must be verified. It is a disguised form of this subjective idealism, although its exponents may not explicitly avow the philosophical attitude which it mirrors. They cautiously step back one stage in their endeavour to approach the subject from the starting-point of consciousness. This backward step becomes Objective Idealism. To them the world exists as an objective reality, and mind *external* to it functioning independently, probing here and there independently. " We can most simply interpret consciousness," says Sir James Jeans, " as something residing entirely outside the picture, and making contact with it only along the world lines of our bodies," and again : " The outstanding achievement of twentieth-century physics is the recognition that we are not yet in contact with ultimate reality."

On this view, the underlying reality of the universe is never perceived ; it baffles investigation at close quarters. A mere appearance is experienced, so that what the mind pictures is not reality, but its superficial structure. The mind probes here and there, gaining impressions, and these are synthesised into objects—not real objects, but mere mental constructs. Only the mind is truly known at close quarters. Mind stuff thus lies at the root of what we are pleased to term the common-sense world, but the essential substance of things is a mystery. "The Universe can be best pictured," says the same writer, "as consisting of pure thought, the thought of what, for want of a wider word, we must describe as a mathematical thinker." Sir Arthur Eddington adopts a view not very different from this. His contention is that, since mathematics deals with abstractions of the common-sense world, representing these as symbols and relations between symbols, the world of science, the scientific picture of the universe, is yet another unreal world, one which in some way violates the common sense of the world of appearance. With the implied claim in both these attitudes that the mathematician's picture of the universe is also that of the scientist, a claim that has been allowed to stand without challenge, principally because of the dominance that the mathematician has established in our generation over the experimentalist, I shall deal in the sequel. The view of the world familiar to common sense is being assailed on all sides, not alone by direct scientific discovery and the new ranges of experience this has opened up, but by the interpretations that are being placed by scientists themselves on the significance of their work. These explanations of the meaning of science have invariably assumed, either tacitly or explicitly, that the idealist framework is the only scheme of the universe into which scientific discovery can be fitted. To a scientist unconcerned with the wider issues of his work such matters would appear to be of little moment. They are philosophy, and not science. Each can proceed with his individual field of inquiry undisturbed by the hair-splitting bickerings of those who are interested in such questions. This is a short-sighted view. The ever-growing fashion for purely mathematical explanation in science is raising an issue that may have serious repercussions in the domain of the experimentalist. The time has now arrived when scientists themselves will require to examine carefully the path they are treading. More than this. Science has transformed and is being used to transform social life. It can be used to destroy masses of humanity by direct war-like action or by organising scarcity and want among large masses of the community driven out of employment. To those who suffer it, all this misery is real, irrational though it be. It cannot be argued out of existence either by denying it or by ignoring it.

CHAPTER II

UNPICKING THE THREADS : THE PROCESS OF ISOLATION

§ 1.

THE tempo of scientific activity during the past decade is a feature peculiar to our time. Side by side with a whirlwind conquest over the brute forces of nature, and a consequent transformation in productive methods that amounts almost to a revolution, there has developed a reorganisation of our notions of Time, Space, and Matter that has transformed them out of all possible likeness to the familiar ideas of these entities we are accustomed to accept in our day to day tasks. To the plain man, to whom such theories are a constant source of unintelligible wonder, their " truth " rests on the practical achievements of science—the telephone, the wireless, television, the aeroplane. To those better informed, other and more difficult problems emerge. Baulked in the attempt to understand the Relativity and Quantum Theories by the technical intricacies of the Tensor Calculus and of non-commutative

Algebra, they must needs fall back on the exposition of interpreters. Considering the abstruse nature of the problems involved, and the apparently revolutionary implications of the solutions that are offered, this is no trivial matter. Space is finite in extent. Space and Time must be welded into a continuous whole. The Universe is a bubble which has already burst. Free-will activity is exhibited in electronic behaviour. Science has given up Determinism. The Architect of the Universe is a Pure Mathematician. These are the phrases that abound in popular scientific exposition, and if they are an accurate representation of the findings of Science, a revolution has certainly occurred in the field of physical inquiry.

For those who wish to understand the philosophical repercussions of modern scientific theory, it is important to recognise two things. On the one hand, too many interpreters, as I have pointed out, have examined the conclusions of science through the spectacles of one particular philosophy, usually of an idealistic nature—concerning which science in the restricted sense has directly little or nothing to say, although, in a wider sense, it cannot escape the problem, as we shall see. On the other hand, many of them, certainly the more eminent, have not distinguished the findings of mathematics sufficiently clearly from the findings of physical science. By profession and mentality, mathematicians, they have forged a colossal weapon of thought that has tended to obscure the physical basis on which the whole structure rests, and science and the modern world have taken on the appearance of a terrifying mathematical theorem.

Scientific work, broadly speaking—internal scientific work, I shall call it—falls naturally under three headings. There is first the purely repetitive class of work, the work of sorting, classification, and accurate measurement of already well-recognised phenomena. Such work includes that undertaken by an analytical chemist, whose business it is to state which known substances and how much of each is contained in a given mixture or compound; it includes also the calibration of clinical thermometers, the determination of the expansion of metals, or their variation in elasticity with temperature—the spadework of science, in fact. Although we are not here concerned with the manipulative skill involved in these operations, which is usually very high, we have to remember that the validity of the conclusions of other branches of science rests ultimately on accurate work of this nature. Many an important discovery, moreover, has arisen from the recognition of a peculiarity in behaviour of a specimen when dealt with at this stage. There is in addition the class of work known as experimental research, where, under carefully controlled laboratory conditions, new characteristics of matter, or little-understood relationships between characteristics, are isolated and exposed. Thus an experimenter may examine the functioning of the kidney in the human body, the transmissibility of certain characteristics from one generation of guinea-pigs to another, the possibility of punching an electron out of matter, the slipping of one layer of a metal crystal over another, the origin of eddying in the air, and so on.

In both of these classes, one in many ways hardly distinguishable from the other, the worker is more or less in direct contact with the material he has to handle. The operations he evolves for exposing to direct perception the phenomenon he is investigating constitute the empirical scientific method. The language of description he uses, the concepts in terms of which he " explains " what is happening, are usually, although not always, expressed in terms of physically experimental operations, and their magnitudes in terms of numbers on a measuring scale or on some form of time-piece. We shall return to this later. For the moment it suffices to recognise that it is the experimenter, the worker on the job, who makes closest contact with the " stuff " under consideration, and the proof that this or that is a characteristic of it is provided in terms of actual physical processes. He does not argue a characteristic into existence. He exposes it by a physical process. If any conclusion is arrived at by argument, the attempt is made to ensure, if possible, that each step in the discussion, each physical property referred to in the discussion, should correspond to a distinct activity that brings to view its existence and its place in the analysis. It is important to recognise the essentially physical nature of the experimentalist's logic. A mathematical proof unbacked and unchecked by physical experience has little standing, if any.

The third class of scientific work is what might be called the Theory of Law-making. Here, if anywhere, is the field of speculation. Here various phases of the experimental evidence, provided in the first two classes, are seized upon and collated. If possible, generalisations, which link together under one head masses of apparently diverse experimental data, are then proposed. Within this field the advances in science are often most spectacular : Newton's Law of Motion generalised partly from a mass of experimental data, partly from *a priori* assumptions ; the Law of Gravitation not from the fictitious fall of an apple, but from the observational data of Tycho Brahe and Kepler; Faraday's and Maxwell's Laws of Electromagnetic action; the Conservation of Matter and of Energy; the Atomic Theory; the Theory of Evolution; the Mendelian Theory; the Electronic Constitution of the Atom; the Theory of Relativity and its generalisations concerning the nature of Time and Space.

Associated with all three categories of scientific workers are accessory branches, concerned with the actual tools of investigation. There are the makers, developers, and refiners of scientific instruments emerging into being under the driving force of scientific practice. There is the expanding field of mathematics itself, mathematical technique breaking out in innumerable directions, opened up at one time by the needs of mathematical expression in physical science, at another by the increasing demand for mathematical tools themselves, and not least by the practical attempts on the part of mathematicians to evolve a mathematical system, logical, complete, self-contained, and isolated from any possible restrictions of Time and Space. It is yet again the search for the Absolute, but one whose perpetual pursuit is for ever fruitful as a driving force in mathematical evolution. Mathematics has been called the Queen of the Sciences.

There are again the technological forms of applied science, the weapons of production, the machinery of factory, workshop, and power-station, evoked on the one hand from science by the social and material needs of man, and on the other stimulated into application by the gathering pressure of scientific discovery.

It would convey a false impression if it were supposed that these three headings into which scientific work has been classified corresponded to distinct modes of approach completely isolated from each other. This is very far from the true position. There is little experimental investigation of any consequence to the scientific movement that does not proceed on some theory of the processes at work. Experiments are not performed in scientific darkness. Each step is illumined directly by the light shed by its predecessor towards a presupposed objective, and indirectly by the breaking dawn of the scientific movement.

The final discovery may turn out quite unexpectedly to be the reverse of what was anticipated, as when Michelson and Morley found that the speed of light did not depend on the forward or backward motion of the Earth from which it was measured. There was, nevertheless, a preliminary theory on which the experiment was erected, and the explanation of the results and its interpretation within the general field of science is expressed in terms of that theory. The practical experiment constitutes the test of the theory, and in general the test is of a numerical nature, although it need not necessarily be so. A theory of a numerical nature is always framed in mathematical terms. Thus all forms of investigations, technological, experimental, theoretical, and mathematical, are interlocked, although, in order to expose more clearly the fact and nature of their presence, we have conceived them as distinct.

§ 2.

The world of common sense has a twofold appearance. It is permanent and it is variable. It is in a continual state of flux, it is dynamic, incessantly changing, a world of perpetual novelty. By its very nature nothing is ever repeated, nothing remains the same. Such is the world we have to accept, the environment in which we find ourselves. Of it we are an essential part. In its evolution within this milieu Mankind has separated from this flowing process aspects that at first sight appear distinct and incapable of intermixture . . . Space, Time, and Matter as the occupant of both. How he has come to make just this form of separation is itself an interesting problem in evolution. It is not improbably associated with two general characteristics that impress themselves on him in the changing world.

Certain transformations occur slowly, or at least so slowly in relation to his own movements or the rapidity of his own reactions that they present stable features in a fickle, uncertain environment. Seizing on the permanent, these he has called *objects*, provided them with names that have become embedded in the language, and in so doing fixed them for succeeding generations. The existence of separate objects occupying permanently, as it seems, definite regions provides us easily with the first aspect, *space*. Other features show a different form of permanence. They come and go, but their appearance and their departure are so systematic that again they also offer something stable, something whose recurrence can be relied upon. The sun rises and sets, the seasons return with persistent regularity, and from this sequence emerges the second aspect of the world—the beating of Time. In the same way we may seize on an individual, oneself, and, granting it an identity, review its history as its dynamic process is revealed; or we may fasten on the world as a static picture and scan the distribution of objects in space.

This separation of matter occupying space and time as if they were independent and isolated entities is a public affair. It is a separation by man as he encounters it, and in that special sense it is an artificial separation. This does not mean that space and time do not really exist, that they are fictitious, but rather that the nature of the separation is one which man, within the limitations of the field he has experienced, has extracted from the world process. As he analyses the universe about him man finds himself envisaging these two apparently separate isolated aspects. He calls this a common-sense view, but it is not so universal as he might imagine. His experience is of course very limited indeed, but even within that narrow range he has never yet experienced a timeless object or a period of time not marked off by objects in space, like the hands of a clock. Space and time coexist as complementary systems extracted from the changing world process, and their assumed independence will remain valid, provisionally and as a practical proposition, just as long as mankind encounters nothing in the universe that forces him to reconsider their isolation.

§ 3.

Time may be subdivided after our own fashion. A pendulum is set oscillating so that it beats out the same number of strokes between successive appearances of the sun over the horizon. That pendulum we may take as a public clock registering the number of strokes that have been made, and thereby dividing Time up into elementary intervals. Time then shows itself merely by the continual registration of the same event between successive larger events. There is only one direction to Time, viz., that in which the number registered increases. To suggest that the direction of Time, or, as Eddington prefers to call it, the arrow of Time, may be uncertain, or is reversible, is to imply that Time is something completely independent of the unfolding process in nature from which the notion has been abstracted. The direction of time is involved in the sequence of events that constitute our universe, and unidirectional time is drawn with time by us from that process. They are inseparable. In his *Nature of the Physical World*, Eddington toys at some length with the notion that the time series may be reversible and that we may remain unaware of this. The idea seems to acquire a specious validity as a real problem from the fact that the mathematical equations that describe the so-called mechanical processes of nature, excluding heat processes, could be interpreted equally well if time were reversed. As far as these equations are concerned, they describe the successive motions of the world machine running forwards or running backwards. They make no distinction between them. The Earth, for example, circling around a lone sun might run in either direction. The equations are the same whether time be increasing positively or negatively. To overcome this apparent indeterminacy, Eddington deems it necessary to bring into operation an additional physical factor as a criterion of direction, what is known as the Law of Entropy. In effect this law states that, as Time increases in any system, the amount of heat-energy available for the performance of useful work diminishes. Thus if a series of bodies is at different temperatures, so that a machine could be run by allowing heat to pass from the warmer bodies to the colder ones, the energy available in this way would continually decrease, the distribution of heat becoming more and more uniform. It is, in fact, by an extrapolation of this law over vast ranges of Space and Time that the death of the universe by heat uniformity has been predicted. *Before* and *after* would correspond to greater and smaller capacity of a system to perform work in virtue of its irregular heat distribution. According to Eddington, if there is a doubt whether two stages of the universe correspond respectively to *Earlier* and *Later*, or vice versa, all that is necessary is to measure the Entropy, and its relative magnitudes at the two stages will resolve for us the puzzle that the ordinary mathematical equations are unable to meet.

Discussion along these lines, it seems to me, betrays an extraordinary confusion between the physics of the real world and the form in which mathematicians attempt to describe it. Time and Time's arrow indissolubly associated are given to us in the unfolding processes we encounter. They represent the recognition by mankind that these processes occur and the process involves the order. The intervals between events may be different for onlookers in different circumstances. That is a matter for experimental study, for a comparison of individual methods of measurement, but the *order* of the events is imposed on us and is common to us all. It is truly impersonal; and without this identity in order we could not use the conception of Time in science at all. That is a feature mankind has found and has to accept. If the ordinary mathematical equations as they are usually formulated fail to embody this feature of the time sequence, that is a weakness of the mathematics, and has nothing whatever to do with the fact that man is directly aware of the order in the time series. The Law of Entropy is of course a very valuable generalisation of experimental fact, but its validity rests not on any *a priori* knowledge, but on a certain broad basis of experiment. For this purpose apparatus has had to be set up, and observations and measurements taken. To suggest that only by means of this Law are we enabled to mark a distinction between events *Before* and *After*, is to suggest that the experimenters were ignorant of the order in which their apparatus was set up, and of whether their observations were taken before or after the experiment ! The fact is that the mathematicians' equations are merely attempts to formulate the changing processes of the universe in concise form, in a form suitable for predictions. In so far as the direction of Time's arrow is absent from his equations, the mathematician may require, and he does require, to supplement them by associating them with some such experimental law as that of Entropy.   The difficulty is of purely mathematical origin.   Presented as a problem of the physical universe it is a suitable fantasy for a Wellsian novel.   If the mathematical equations are unable to state for us in which direction the earth rotates around the sun, that is simply because the equations necessarily treat the sun and earth as practically isolated from the rest of the system, and definitely and completely isolated in time from their earlier history that involves the stages leading up to the present situation.

§ 4.

Science, like common sense, sets out in the first instance to search for systems that can be imagined as isolated from their setting in the universe without appreciably disturbing their structure and the process they present. Here is a child. Almost as soon as the term child has been applied to it we have effected the isolation, for, in thought at any rate, we have dismissed its history, its family relationships, its home, and its country. We have isolated it by classifying it in this case, by merging it tentatively with other objects under the general heading CHILD. It can itself now be further separated into isolated systems. If we examine its hair, the colour of its eyes, its digestive system, we are by that process forming in succession new isolated sub-systems. The isolation is only tentative in thought, and is conducted for purposes of discussion in the first instance, and for convenience in detailed examination. The process of formation of such systems, moreover, may even be carried on until the limits of scientific measurement are reached. From the hair we may proceed to its internal texture, its chemical composition, its atomic structure. Any object is in this sense an isolated system, irrespective of size, but it may nevertheless not be a system useful for scientific practice. That, as we shall see in a moment, depends on certain other factors to which we have not yet referred. When, as above, the object is a child, each one of the subsidiary systems may of course be regarded as one of its characteristics, one of its properties, and, if we so care to express it, we can say that these are elements of its individuality. This method of isolation by detailed classification does not destroy individuality or uniqueness. It merely examines it by disclosing the *unique combination* of isolated systems that the object possesses. Here is an antique oak table, in many ways unique. Although I classify each of these into recognised categories, I do not destroy its uniqueness by isolating, in discussion, the surface polish, the texture of the wood, the shape of the legs.

It is sometimes argued that the method of science is in reality merely a method of classification, that objects and their characteristics are classified into groups, pre-existent groups, and that therefore its very essence, the unique characteristics of any entity, that make it just itself, and in virtue of which it differs from everything else, are necessarily ignored by science. Dealing only with the common elements, it can be concerned only with superficial structure, and the inner substance eludes it. There is a mystery that science cannot probe. If all the characteristics that science separates out were finally aggregated together, they would not reconstitute the original entity. Its essential substantiality would be missing, its organised wholeness would be absent. I shall deal in the sequel with some of the numerous misinterpretations of the scientific method involved in this statement. Here it suffices to state that every isolated system, every isolate is itself unique in its mode of functioning, otherwise it would not be isolated, and it is a unique combination of its sub-isolates. It has therefore a uniqueness in the fact of what it is observed to possess, in the unique manner in which it operates, and in no other sense, just as a moving point has a uniqueness in virtue of its changing specification in position. Uniqueness, to be spoken of at all, requires words to describe it, and the existence of the necessary nouns already involves the fact that the unique elements have been classified. There is nothing new in this aspect of science. It is the common-sense method of examin--

ation in everyday life, and it is implicit in speech; for every ordinary noun is representative of a class. Science has explored the usefulness of this method and its consequences on a larger scale than that of " common sense."

What constitutes an isolated system that is scientifically useful? All the characteristics we have dealt with so far have been in a sense positive. Here is a tobacco jar standing on the table. It has a circular top. The shape of the top is an isolated system if it can be studied, as it were, on its own, by ignoring the jar. Can it? I remove the tobacco jar from the table, and there is no measurable difference produced on the shape of the top—it is still circular. The system behaves neutrally to that part of its environment, and in thought we can strip the two apart. We can ignore the table, necessary as it is for other purposes. I examine the jar-top to-day and a week hence, and there is no appreciable change in circularity. Its position has been changed in space and in time, and there is no alteration in the shape of our selected system; it is capable of being neutrally and therefore validly isolated, for scientific purposes. To justify this isolation I have had in the first place to resort to direct test by experiment. The shape of the jar-top had to be measured in order to verify its independence of time and place, but to do so it had to be brought into close contact with something else—a measuring rod. If every time I measure the jar-top with the rod the same measurement is found, we are entitled equally well to assert that the rod is isolated and neutral with respect to the jar-top. We are so accustomed to find isolated systems of this type in connection with measuring apparatus, and unconsciously to take only such systems, that we sometimes forget that circumstances may arise when it may not be possible at all to find them.

In the first place, every measuring instrument must be neutral to the system measured. We do not choose a red-hot foot-rule to measure the length of a block of ice, although, as we shall see in a moment, we may reasonably do so, in certain circumstances. Every scientific instrument, moreover, must form, *with* the system it is expected to measure, an isolated neutral system. An ammeter, for example, is to be used for the measurement of an electric current. The ammeter, the wires, and the current have to form an isolated system, otherwise we will find " errors " in the measurement, the ammeter will be " disturbed," and the currents " affected." Every good experimenter has to compensate for all sorts of extraneous effects that enter into his experiments—slight changes in temperature in the room during the progress of the test, draughts, vibration of the building, heat radiation from the body of the experimenter himself, and so on. All these are merely methods of allowing for an environment that is not truly neutral. They constitute the experimental technique of *isolation*. On the theoretical side the search for isolated systems is carried still further when it deals with entities such as particles, atoms, electrons, genes and points, chromosomes, circles, spheres, steady motion, forces. None of these ever exists in isolation, but, in its game of breaking down the complex processes of nature, in its search for isolation, science has invented these and has found them useful. There is no such thing as a mere sphere. There are spherical bodies.

§ 5.

Natural science is not unique in its search for isolated systems. It is a characteristic of every form of analysis. It is the method we adopt in ordinary discussion. We talk of objects, tables and chairs, as if they were systems neutral to their environments. We shift our furniture from one house to another, and the shape of the table and the comfort of the easy-chair are unaffected by the change of location. We take it for granted because we have found it is so.

If the softness of an easy-chair varied with the room in which it was placed it is possible that we should not regard it as the completely separate and isolated object we do. We might possibly widen the conception of chair to chair-room, or, if it changed in numerous respects as it passed from room to room as a puff of air changes in shape, we might discard the concept *chair* as being useless for purposes of discussion. The beauty of a picture, again, may vary with the setting. Our individual appreciation of it may vary with our physical condition in some way. We do not require to be able to measure *appreciation of beauty* to be able to recognise this. All that requires to be pointed out is that we and the picture in this respect are not isolated one from the other or from the environments in which we and it are found.

§ 6.

A tree is virtually an isolated system as long as we are concerned with the lesser systems we can derive from it by further analysis—the bark, the shape and colour of the leaves, its fruit, its girth, its age, and the number of its annular rings. As soon as we are concerned with its growth process, however, we have to take into account its roots and the atmosphere in which it grows. We have to widen the system so as

c

to embrace more of that environment than previously was regarded as neutral to it. We have to take in sufficient of the soil in the region of the roots to provide us with yet another neutral system. We have to include certain characteristics of the air in the neighbourhood of the leaves to provide a neutral system. Not all the atmosphere of the universe is needed for this purpose, and not all the soil of the earth. The vital question of course is how much precisely of each has to be included. That again is a matter of experiment, a scientific matter, just as it was necessary to take the tobacco jar from off the table to verify that the circular shape of the top was neutral to the table on which the jar stood. *The first function of experimental inquiry is, if possible, to find precisely how little of an environment need be included to render a system neutral.*

The whole technique of experiment is concerned with that. It never, in fact, attains this ideal, for the simple reason that there are no *absolutely* isolated systems unless it be the whole universe. Science does, in fact, find circumstances in which they can be delimited with great precision. Scientific laws and scientific facts are all statements concerning such systems, perfected, idealised. Boyle's Law for Gases, for example, states that if a given volume of gas is subjected to pressure, as in a bicycle pump, the volume is halved if the pressure is doubled, and the volume is doubled if the pressure is halved. There is a reciprocal relation between pressure and volume. The law is always qualified by the statement that throughout the course of the experiment the temperature of the gas must remain unchanged, but there are numerous other restrictions that have to be imposed at the same time, although they are considered to be so obvious that they are never referred to. The constant temperature of the gas has to be above a certain minimum value, otherwise the nature of the gas will undergo a change under pressure. It will liquefy and the law will cease to apply. The quantity of the gas has to remain unchanged throughout the experiment. There must, for example, be no leak in the vessel containing the gas, nor must any of it become embedded or occluded, as it is called, in the walls of the vessel, and so on. The gas, in fact, has to be an isolated system, divorced from the rest of the universe, for clearly even the presence of the experimenter and the heat that radiates from his body may affect the temperature of the gas. The law is in this sense an idealised one, and therefore it is not surprising that in practice it is never found to be quite truly fulfilled. It is an approximation to the greater reality.

Scientific truth is not an idealised truth to which

the universe closely approximates, it is a first
step in the process of finding out the truth about
the universe by examining it in chips. The first
step is succeeded by a second more detailed, more
refined. It embraces yet a little more of the
changing environment as soon as it finds that its
initial law is not precisely fulfilled, for by that failure
it recognises that the isolation was not neutral. It
sees, for example, that there are effects arising from
the changing temperature of the gas, so it turns to an
examination of the changes in volume and of pressure
that follow from such changes. Its isolated system,
or its isolate as we will call it, is now a gas of varying
temperature, pressure, and volume, but otherwise
the same restrictions apply as heretofore and it sets
up a new and wider law. It produces Gay-Lussac's
Law, which describes exactly how pressure and
volume jointly depend on the temperature of the gas.
More than this, the law involves Boyle's Law as a
special case, when the temperature is supposed constant and unchanging. And so the game proceeds.
More and more of the environment is allowed within
the precincts of the isolated system as soon as it has
become clear, by an examination of the world of
actuality, that the present stage of the law does not
fulfil the actual conditions with sufficient precision.
Thus each neutral system becomes wider than that

preceding it. Each earlier one becomes a sub-system of that which follows, and laws of wider and wider generality emerge. They relate to a greater and greater range of environment, and a greater and greater degree of apparent complexity. The existence of the more general law is evidence that this has been rearranged as a broad but simple scheme.

§ 7.

The pursuit of science is frequently regarded as a detailed examination of the properties of matter. Properties are characteristics presumed to be wrapped up with the object indissolubly, the latter carrying them about with it wherever it goes and whenever it is, and reacting in their individual ways in the environments in which it is placed. The object is thus a self-contained entity existing of its own right and embodying all the characteristics, all the properties, that make it just itself.

It is curious that this word "property" should have become so deeply embedded in the literature of science. It owes its origin and its use in these connections to the close link that has existed between science and philosophy in the early days of science. It is an unfortunate word, for several reasons that are not very apparent to scientific men, simply because they have become so habituated to its use. In many ways it is an unnecessary word, for in general these so-called properties are only regularities in behaviour. *Water has the property of expanding when it freezes*, is merely an unnecessarily abstruse way of saying—*Water expands on freezing*. Again, *Rubber has the property of dissolving in carbon bisulphide* and *carbon bisulphide has the property of dissolving rubber* may be stated as *Rubber dissolves in carbon bisulphide*.

The word *Property* in this way appears as a subtle method of fixing ownership for a form of behaviour either on to the object (rubber) or on to the environment (carbon bisulphide) or on to both. Instead of saying " In certain circumstances it behaves," we find ourselves saying, " It has the property that . . . " In science, unlike literature, mere verbosity is not necessarily an evil in itself. It becomes a danger when it is used for false emphasis, and the continual use of the word property may provide just that false emphasis that extracts the behaviour from the stage of being mutual, environmental, and active to that of being individually fixed and proprietary. It becomes akin to private property. It is not necessarily a valid separation, but it may be, and in fact is, a very useful method of study and investigation. Its validity must be put to the test of experiment. We have to pursue the study of the object through its varying environments in order to discover whether its fluctuating behaviour in these circumstances can be consistently attributed to *invariant and unchanging* properties attached to the body. Here, for example, is a small piece of matter, the size of a pinhead. If dropped it falls to Earth in its own peculiar way. Here is a larger mass we call a ball. It also behaves in its own way when thrown across a cricket pitch. Can these so-called properties of the cricket ball be *explained* or *accounted for* in terms of those of the particle? Are they " consistent " with the properties of the particle? There is a huge mass, the Earth, in motion relative to the Sun, here are a concourse of innumerable planets, suns, and diffuse nebulæ. Can the vast panorama we call the mutual behaviour of the solar system be completely accounted for or referred back to the invariant properties we have attached to the particle? The fact that science attempts to do so is of course merely stating again that the method of isolation is itself characteristic of the scientific method. It is once more the search for permanence in a fluctuating and changing environment. Science attempts to attain that permanence by isolating aspects of the behaviour that can be regarded as unchanging and fastening them as properties on the object. It may be here, or it may be there, radiating its " properties " and producing its characteristic effects on whatever it encounters. From this angle the Laws of Science may then be regarded as the rules of combination of such propertied objects, the rules expressing their interaction.

§ 8.

Various forms of isolates can be distinguished, although these forms are not in effect neutrally isolated from each other. While the natural mode of approach would be to examine first the essentially practical forms in which these manifest themselves, since scientific theory is largely an expanding outgrowth from that, it will be easier in the first instance to reverse the procedure.

There are, in the first place, the purely theoretical isolates, atoms and electrons, with all the properties which one attaches to them in order to allow for the environment from which they have sprung. There are isolates like motion and position separated off from the moving body—sub-isolates, in fact—and handled as continuous entities. There are forces which the mathematician will handle in isolation, combining them according to the rules, or in other words according to the properties that forces are presumed to possess. These are all of a highly theoretical nature and are themselves represented by symbols or diagrams on a sheet of paper and dealt with in this new isolated medium. The rules for the combination of the forces become rules for the connecting up of lines. The isolate has itself in the first instance emerged from actual practical experience with bodies in the physical world. Two billiard balls meet in impact, and the theoretician isolates from them merely what he would call the impulse on impact, and examines what effect is thus produced on that other isolate he calls the motion. The theoretical isolates emerge when the need shows itself for " explaining " some form of behaviour in the practical world or in the world of experiment. These may appear to be very far removed from practical affairs, but they may be very vital to the practice of the scientist.

There are, next, the isolates of the experimenter. His measuring instruments, for example, are in effect attempts to obtain self-contained isolated systems, thermometers and barometers to measure temperature and pressure, themselves isolates of the medium with which he has to deal. If experimental investigation is to proceed, scientific instruments must be produced, for the vital process in scientific research is to discover what qualities may be isolated and measured and to produce for it a measuring system as far as possible devoid of "errors." These errors, as we have seen, are evidence of the lack of neutrality in the isolate. If measurement is an essential feature of the practice of science, the formation of experimental isolates is a necessary condition for its success. A whole experiment, and not merely the individual measuring parts of it, is the isolate, for if an experiment is to produce results of practical value to science it must be so conducted as to allow appropriately for the environment. It must be neutral to it. Hence a good experimenter always takes great trouble to allow for fluctuating disturbances and to eliminate "errors."

The work of the experimenter is to separate out measurable isolates. He takes a sunbeam, for example, concentrating only on its brightness. He passes it through a glass prism, and studies its spectrum, the band of rainbow colour stretching from deep violet at the one extremity to deep red at the other. Everything else, as it were, is dismissed in view of the fact that the same distribution of colouring and of brightness can be obtained with a whole series of prisms, and with sunbeams taken on different days. The spectrum only is his isolate. A study of this by means of a telescope shows that the coloured band is traversed at various positions by fine dark lines. These were discovered by Fraunhofer. If all beams of light, however produced, whether from the sun or artificially, produced the same spectrum with the same dark lines, the beam would indeed be completely isolated neutrally from its source, but this is not so. If, for example, the light is produced from incandescent molten iron, a spectrum is indeed obtained, but, if some of the metal turn to vapour, instead of dark lines, bright lines are found in certain positions across the colour band. Thus the distribution of the colours appears to be capable of neutral isolation, but the transverse lines are not. They must form a system *with* the source of light, the lines being merely sub-isolates. It is unnecessary to enter into detailed explanations here. It suffices to state that by a further system of isolated experiments, experiments which were concentrated entirely on the production of the isolated dark and bright lines, it has been possible to show that certain metals such as iron must be present in the form of incandescent vapour in the Sun since the sub-isolates can be detected in the light they emit. This work conducted by Kirchhof and Bunsen has in fact given rise to the whole branch of analysis known as Spectroscopy, whereby chemical substances are recognised by a very definite isolate, the positions of bright lines that are found in their spectrum when the substances are heated to incandescent vapour.

The third form of isolate to which we must refer is of an even more practical nature. It emerges in production particularly, and is seen in the numerous forms of industrial specialisation. The vanishing of the craftsman and his displacement by a host of machines which each carries through one isolated portion of the whole work, the elimination of the human worker by the steady process of division and sub-division of simple operations corresponds merely to a recognition of the possibility of forming these isolates in practice and of regarding the final total assembly of these parts, each one of which may be independently, and therefore neutrally effected, as itself an isolated step. Every form of specialisation is a form of isolation. Finally there are isolates of a sociological nature to which we shall return when we endeavour to assess the significance of the scientific movement in that field.

§ 9.

An electric charge existing of its own right alone in an infinite space is presumed to have a field of force radiating outwards ready to attract or repel any unlike or like charge that may be placed in that

region with it. Such an idealised charge has, in fact, no environment, it is a completely isolated system, but the environment from which we imagine it to have been plucked is tentatively represented by this attractive property of the charged and completely isolated particle. Starting from this element, theory endeavours to build up more complicated systems by combining them according to the rules it has laid down as applicable to the properties of each isolated element. It is, of course, clear that, if theory should fail in its effort to construct more complicated processes from these elements, the cause of that failure must reside in the fact that it is endeavouring to reverse a process of subdivision, the formation of isolated systems, by merely tacking on properties of a simple and constant nature to the elements. Actually the method has proved to be enormously successful. A vast mass of astronomical prediction rests upon it. The striking success of theoretical chemistry depends on the assumption that there are ninety-two different elements or atoms, to each of which may be attached properties exhibited by comparatively large masses of these substances. If, in all the chemical combinations we have investigated, it is always found that the smallest proportions of oxygen, hydrogen, nitrogen, chlorine that occur in action are 1 of hydrogen, 16 of oxygen, 14 of nitrogen, 32 of chlorine,

it seems pertinent to fix such numbers to a hypothetical entity we call the atom or the molecule according to circumstances, and to examine whether the concept of such units of each substance with unchanging properties can be used for constructing more complicated combinations, and for predicting in what circumstances these will be found. Such a procedure, which lies at the root of the whole atomic theory of matter, has been attended with remarkable success.

In spite of all this, however, the method is clearly subject to such possible restrictions that we can have little justification for expecting it to succeed in all circumstances we may encounter. It implies throwing the whole onus of the gross behaviour of matter in the enormously complex environments in which it is found on to a relatively small number of invariant properties of these usually hypothetical elements. As we penetrate deeper and deeper into the constitution of matter, increasing the demands on the finer and finer elements that are separated out as so-called isolated systems, serious difficulties are encountered in the attempt to reconstruct, in theory, the behaviour of the grosser mass. Mathematicians, for example, are demanding a combined space-time with as many as seven dimensions for a full representation of the interaction of two electrons, iso-

lated from the rest of the universe. What kind of a universe will be required to accommodate a simple matchbox can scarcely be imagined! It is not, however, the two electrons that require seven dimensions, but the mathematicians! They are the reality here, and it is their behaviour—that is, their mathematical theory—that is in question. If, in the development of their theories, they make demands on the Universe so exorbitant that the experimenter cannot meet these claims, then repudiation may be his only alternative. For in the last resort he is the arbiter.

§ 10.

From the standpoint here adopted we see that the great adventure of science lies in the query, "Are there any processes in Nature that cannot be adequately explored by seeking for isolated systems neutral to their environment?" Since the discovery of such a system rests ultimately on experiment, it is in experiment that the answer must be sought. We have to await the advent of such a case. There are, however, certain dangers that require to be anticipated if an answer is not to be thrust on us prematurely. I have stated that every piece of apparatus, if it is to function, must remain neutral to the environment it is to measure. A yard-stick is regarded as such a system. It would fail in its function if the measurements it provided of the length of this page differed widely on successive occasions of measurement. If two yard-sticks whose markings coincided one with the other did not give consistent measurements of the same object, itself presumably an isolated system, we should be driven to the conclusion not necessarily that there was something mysterious in the operations of the universe, but that we had still to seek the appropriate systems. In ordinary speech we would say they were affecting each other.

In the street white flakes are falling steadily. I stretch out my warm hand to examine them, and discover that they are merely drops of water. Allowed to fall on a sheet of cold metal, they are small flakes of snow. A sheet of ice is stretched out and the particles that fall are frozen. A red-hot plate shows them up as hot spheres of liquid, and a fire as puffs of steam. What, we ask, is this mysterious and fickle entity, that may show itself as ice, snow, water, or steam according to how it is examined? The answer to the riddle is, of course, obvious in this case. These instruments for examining the white flakes have not been neutral, but we have known circumstances in which warm hands, hot plates, cold metal sheets, ice, water, and steam have all been isolated systems, and we use the facts so exposed in such a manner that the various methods of examination suggested here give us consistently neutral systems for isolation. The body of knowledge we call science may therefore enable us to convert a seemingly non-neutral system into a neutral one. We can correct for its errors, as it were. Isolated systems are not then separated out on their merits. Each case is not an individual issue. It is illuminated by the light that a similar process has already shed in other directions. The length of a hot boiler plate may quite accurately be measured by a metal yard-stick, since we have already discovered how such a metal rod will expand when its temperature is raised.

§ 11.

It does not follow from this that the method of isolation will necessarily always be successful, nor, on the other hand, that if it fails there is some supernatural agency at work. Persistent failure to expose how it fails would be a serious matter. It may not be out of place to indicate here and now where it appears that this stage has been reached in connection with these little particles of negative electricity we call electrons. They, as we know, are shot off from matter in the radio-active state, so that they must be regarded as a constituent of these substances. They are never encountered in the isolated state, as individuals, although a track they have presumably traced out may be photographed on a sensitive plate, or a splash as they fall on a luminescent screen may be quite clearly distinguished. In such circumstances they behave like any particle, and therefore in themselves they may be regarded as isolated systems whose characteristics one might expect to resemble those of ordinary particles of matter, except that they are known to hold an electric charge. On this basis therefore may be built up a perfectly definite picture, that fits into the traditional scientific scheme. When they are allowed to impinge on a thin metal film, however, instead of behaving like any self-respecting old-fashioned particle, a new feature emerges. They give rise to a pattern of the type that would be produced if they were in effect the centre of a wave disturbance. Never before in the history of science has anything been encountered that may at one moment act as a discrete and isolated particle and at the next as a wave. We cannot picture it as an entirety. With the possible exception of light itself, to which it is closely related, we have not experienced its like before. Its behaviour does not appear consistent, and consistency of behaviour is an essential for the formation of an isolated system in science. Perhaps it is not precisely correct to say that it is not consistent. In certain circumstances it does behave consistently as a charged particle and in others consistently as a wave. It has, as it were, two separate identities. In two different environments it exhibits vastly different forms of behaviour. In the terminology to which we have been objecting it would be stated that electrons have both particle and wave *properties*. To describe this, the word *wavicle* has been suggested. It is not surprising therefore to discover that science finds itself baulked in its attempt to predict precisely what will happen to such a " particle." It can predict with great assurance what on the average will happen to a crowd of these fickle entities, but the single member evades it.

Why is this? I do not wish here to anticipate the discussion I propose to give later on the place of prediction and determinism in science, but it is worth while noting certain points at this stage. Science, as I have stressed, is basically experimental. Whatever its theories, it never dare proceed with assurance further than experiment can penetrate. When an effort is made to form an isolate from a mass of known data it is to experiment that we must turn to supply the criterion whether the system is indeed neutral and isolated. In the case of the electron we are dealing with the smallest entity perceivable. A single specimen is not seized, held firmly, and studied in detail. They have to be taken as they are found, in exceedingly high states of motion, studied in their passage during incredibly short intervals of time. These intervals of time, as we have explained, are themselves marked off for us by portions of matter signalling events equivalent to the beating of a pendulum. The distances the experimenter has to measure, however they may be obscured, have to be sepa-rated by marks on a scale, and the very apparatus he uses contains vast numbers of the class of object—electrons—he is examining. What basis of evidence can he then have for expecting that the apparatus he uses and the individual object he desires to study, and concerning whose behaviour he desires to make predictions, separately constitute isolated systems? The very process of studying and measur-ing these elementary entities necessarily requires that they must be handled at such close quarters as to disturb the environment we normally presume to be neutral. This shows itself in a variety of ways, but here it is merely necessary to mention one. We have become accustomed to regard the speed and the position of a body as two separate features of its state, two independent isolated systems, and there is good justification for it. With most objects we can study them " at rest " within our environment where the changes in its sub-system occur so slowly in relation to the speed of our perceiving apparatus that their separation appears to be valid. We ignore the changes in the first instance and regard the object as an isolated and permanent and localised system. It may be moving, it may be at rest, but it is an *object* whatever its state of motion.

With an electron, however, no such permanent features have ever been discovered. It is never caught " at rest "—it flashes past at an incredible speed, its mass depends on its speed. It is doubtful whether there could be such an entity as an electron *at rest*. In point of fact when it strikes a metal film and becomes *at rest*, it shows itself as a system of waves, it vanishes as a particle. Here, then, at this level of smallness, position, speed, and mass are not necessarily separable, and we begin to recognise that the permanently isolated systems, object, position, and speed are no longer separately neutral. If we seize on one and insist on regarding such qualities as independent and unchanging, we do so at peril to the others we have ignored. What will happen then if we endeavour to specify accurately the " position " of the electronic " particle " as it is moving? We are likely to find that the more accurate the specification is attempted, the less accurately will we be able to specify its speed. When the speed is the highest possible—the velocity of light—the particle is everywhere. When the speed is zero, the position of the particle cannot be stated. It is no longer a particle. We must not be surprised if, between these two extremes, the theoretical isolate we insist on retaining behaves rather peculiarly.

§ 12.

At this level of investigation, where the search for isolated systems depends on the development of an experimental technique at the extreme limits of our powers of observation even with the most delicate apparatus, we are face to face with unprecedented although not unexpected difficulties in providing the elementary material out of which a theory of action may be constructed. We have begun with the universe of common sense, the universe we apprehend, and we have seen scientific development as the search for isolates in this world process, and as an essential part of this search the determination of environments neutral to the isolated systems. The study of science from this angle becomes as much a scrutiny of environment as a study of objects or systems of objects. Basically it rests on an experimental justification. We have viewed science as a breaking-down process, a chipping off of pieces, and an examination of how small a piece may be chipped off in order yet to be able to state with sufficient precision what is happening in detail to the universe. We have regarded it as a process of analysis, passing from the larger to the smaller, from masses to particles, from particles to atoms, from atoms to electrons. . . . It is the function of the mathematician to build up a theory of all this, to link together the various levels at which behaviour may be described. The experimenter takes the larger entity and knocks the smaller out of it. He exposes the possibility of a sub-system, but he may not necessarily assert that this sub-system is neutrally isolated when taken by itself. A mathematical technique which faithfully described the process of the experimenter would follow this analytic process and show how from the larger isolate the lesser isolate was derived. Almost universally, however, mathematicians have adopted the reverse method. They have regarded science as a building-up process, a synthetic process, electrons with their properties leading to atoms with their properties, and these again leading to particles and masses with their properties. Such was the atomistic method of the Greek materialists who attempted to reconstruct the universe from preconceived elements initially separated from their setting.

§ 13.

A literature may be analysed into books, books into sentences, sentences into words, and words into letters, but the writings of Shakespeare are not by that argument a mere collection of letters. All that one is finally left with was present in the original, but during the analysis something has dropped out. Isolated systems have been formed with the accompanying assumptions of neutrality. The context, so to speak, has been omitted at each stage, the book from its place in the literature, the sentence from its interpretation within the book, and the word from its setting in the sentence. It is clearly futile to expect that we could reverse the process and reconstruct the litera-ture by the game of word-building from the mere isolated letters. While this seems obvious enough, the fact that just this process is applied in science is not always recognised by writers dealing with its philosophy. They are continually disturbed at the idea that as elements are added to elements there emerges from the combination something new. When the atom of oxygen combines with two atoms of hydrogen there "emerges" a molecule of water with all the characteristics that water possesses, but characteristics absent from the original combining gases.

It is a difficulty that the plain man cannot understand. There is no mystery about water and its liquidity. He has bathed in that, and on occasion even drunk it. That at any rate is a tangible reality to him, and if the performing antics of your scientists' atoms will not account for this liquidity, then so much the worse for your atoms. And the peculiar thing is that he is right. We are all very much creatures of habit, especially communal habits, and when several generations of scientific men have spoken and thought in terms of atoms and molecules until these ideas have insinuated themselves into all forms of scientific explanation, they acquire as unchallenged a position among the realities of science as water possesses to the plain man. The fact is, of course, that there are no such entities as atoms of oxygen and hydrogen divorced from the rest of reality, entities by themselves.

There is no experimental justification for regarding these gases in this way as complete isolated entities, unless they already embody as a " property " the fact of their combination into liquid water. Properties, as we have seen, are simply our method of fastening on to the isolated system we propose to invent something which will allow for the environment we have neutralised. The reverse process, the production of oxygen and hydrogen from water, illustrates this. Water is then the more embracing isolated system, and the two sub-systems are the two gases we derive from it. To identify these gases obtained by analysis with the two gases which by synthesis go to form water, implies that the property of " aquosity," as it has been jocularly called, has initially to be associated with the two atoms in isolation. As a serious problem, however, this point is quite trivial. What is at issue is not simply the question why two gases combine to give a liquid, but why in certain circumstances the same mass of material is at one temperature in liquid form and at a higher temperature in gaseous form. For the gases oxygen and hydrogen may be exploded above the boiling point of water to give steam, also a gas. The problem is identical with that which arises when we endeavour to explain how a bar possesses " rigidity " (in place of " aquosity ") if it is composed merely of commonplace atoms loosely hanging together. If it does not explain this, the *simple* atomic concept is false; atoms are not then truly isolated systems.

§ 14.

General Smuts falls into a similar fallacy in what he calls the holistic interpretation of science. " Electrons and protons have massed into matter," he says. " Matter has raised itself to higher elements, and ever higher and more complex compounds. Inert matter has become active living matter. Living organisms have been on the upgrade for the last thousand million years, with steadily rising types of bodily structure and behaviour. And still the road continues to rise upward. Tropisms, reflexes, instincts, intelligence, and finally the crowning glory of the human soul, or personality making for the City of God. . . . In all this we see . . . the laws of logic, of science apparently being violated. We see the more coming out of the less, the something out of the apparent nothing. . . ." Then again : " When elements, parts, constituents . . . coalesce to form a whole they become creative, they produce more than they themselves are."

Here again we see the same surprise expressed by the realisation that life is not necessarily a mere summation of isolated systems. For these electrons and protons and all the other constituents out of which he expects to reconstitute his universe are all mere mathematical fictions in so far as they are presumed to have separated existences. General Smuts, taking his cue from the common scientific outlook, has come to regard them as the prime reality, individual real entities with certain pre-supposed properties. In so far as these isolated entities with *these properties* in isolation are unable to reconstitute his universe, he finds himself driven to see a mystical birth at each stage in the process of aggregation. Somehow or other the character-istics of the larger system have to be accounted for, he feels, in terms of those of the smaller, instead of the converse. Thus he sees " the more coming out of the less," and, with such an unlimited fund of creative strength, the miracle of an ascent to the martyr's crown is not difficult. The meaning of scientific explanation and the whole interpretation of science turn on which of these modes of description fits the facts of the movement we call science.

In their attack on atomism expositors of Holism appear, nevertheless, to accept the conclusions of the atomistic approach as part of their own creed. Holists argue that, if the atomic method is adopted, the process of splitting up ignores an entity, or destroys a state of affairs, referred to variously as Organisation and Co-ordinated Maintenance; that Nature does not proceed by atomic action, but by action in " wholes." How a self-contained " whole " is not itself an atom of a larger " whole " it is not easy to see, nor how, with a continuously interrelated changing environment, there can be either wholes or atoms *absolutely* isolated from the rest of the universe and functioning on their own. The justification for the use of an atomistic or of a holistic method of approach rests initially on the answer to the practical question " Does it work? " There is no immediate criterion for an eminently practical venture like science. A treatment of the circumstances in which a machine will work efficiently and an answer to the question how long that machine will take to perform some piece of work is not met by a study of its atomic interchanges. For that purpose the machine is the whole, or the atom in its environment, but there are other circumstances, in many chemical processes for instance, in which an atomic investigation and explanation may be exceedingly valuable in its practical outcome. To each class of question belongs its appropriate isolate. Holists endeavour to bolster an absolutist philosophy of Wholes merely by exposing the inadequacy of Atomism. To meet a situation that need not arise, they are inevitably driven to postulate a mystical and emergent " more coming out of the less," within the body of these wholes.

It is not to be supposed, of course, that in the wide sense in which I have used the term isolated systems individual scientists *deliberately* seek these out. We are not at the moment concerned with what interpretations individual scientists offer for their actions. We are endeavouring rather to clarify the general mode of scientific investigation as a developed movement quite apart from the detailed plans of the individuals. Most scientists are not conscious of the fact that they work within a larger scheme with a fairly definite method of procedure. They regard themselves as free agents or as the unconscious instruments of a mysterious inner urge.

" Every experimentalist, worthy of the name," writes Dr. Dingle in *Science and Human Experience*, " knows by instinct which is the right road to take." One might imagine from this that Dr. Dingle believed that no scientist worthy of the name ever made a mistake. He does not of course believe this, for, if so, he would likewise hold that every scientist worthy of the name also on occasion knows by instinct what is the wrong road to take, and takes it. At the same level of discussion much is made of the unbiased judgment of the scientist in the balancing of evidence and in its verification, as if individual intellectual equipoise were necessarily an aspect of a corresponding freedom from bias in the scientific movement as a whole. Such matters are dealt with more fully in a later chapter. Here it is necessary merely to state that to most scientists the wider framework is simply an unconscious tradition that they follow unquestioningly. Their behaviour within this framework is then explained by them in purely subjective terms.

CHAPTER III

THE QUEEN OF THE SCIENCES—MATHEMATICS

" If there be some babblers who, though ignorant of all mathematics take upon them to judge of these things, and dare to blame and cavil at my work, because of some passage of Scripture which they have wrested to their own purpose, I regard them not, and will not scruple to hold their judgment in contempt."—Copernicus, *De Revolutionibus* (Dedication to the Pope).

PURE MATHEMATICS is the method of isolation raised to a fine art. Its most fundamental concept is that of number. Not three apples, three lives, or three ideas, but simply *three* isolated from its subject of reference, and written 3. Hence by the direct process of isolation we obtain the sequence of numbers which for shortness we write 1, 2, 3, . . . 100, 101, ...

For even greater brevity we write 10^2 for 100, 10^3 for 1000, 10^6 for 1,000,000, the upper number representing the number of noughts that stand after the 1.

The idea of including zero represented by the symbol 0 among the list of whole numbers came very late in the history of Arithmetic, thousands of years after actual enumeration of at least the simpler sort had become a commonplace. That is not unexpected, for if number is derived by isolation from objects in the real world it could not include zero. Not until isolation had proceeded a stage further did the need for a symbol to represent nothing become felt. That stage was the recognition of the symbols themselves as the objects under consideration. Once the numbers had become mere marks on a sheet of papyrus or beads on a string or wire, the needs of reckoning in barter and exchange found an outlet in the importance to be attached to *position*. Something, for example, had to replace the empty column in the reckoning board, something had to stand for the presence of a gap, and so the epoch-making invention of the zero 0 saw the light.

We who have been brought up from childhood to the arithmetical habit and to the decimal system, writing 10 as naturally as we write 1, and giving a significance to the new environment of 1 in 10, scarcely realise that the use of 0 among the list of figures and the interpretation we now unconsciously place on the position of figures in a number make it possible to write any number up to, say, 1,234,567,890 with no more than ten symbols instead of with one thousand two hundred and thirty-four millions five hundred and sixty-seven

D

thousand eight hundred and ninety symbols. The history of commerce and industry, the history of science and of culture, would have been far different without it. It was a revolutionary step in the history of writing, in the development of social communication and intercourse. We in our day have become so habituated to it that we are not merely ignorant of the identity of the inventor and benefactor to humanity, but usually quite unaware of its profound importance.

Such is the language of Arithmetic. Mathematics in its wider development goes much further in the process of isolation. It dismisses the individual number when it wishes to speak merely of *a number* irrespective of which one it actually is. It isolates the fact of the number and says that n, or a, or x is any number. This is what is called an algebraic symbol, but that is nothing more than the statement that n is a short word, the shortest one we can find, for the words " any number."

It appears, then, that the first few steps in mathematical symbolism are at one and the same time a direct application of the process of isolation and a method for finding a convenient form of speech for the subject of discourse. In this respect we are following the practice of ordinary speech where each noun in the language stands for an isolated system. The difference so far enters merely in this way. First that mathematical language is one of short symbols for isolates in place of the longer ones of common speech, and secondly the symbols stand for numbers.

In physical science no measurement, no scientific result can be divorced from the process of arriving at it. When we say that a building is 100 feet high, we imply much more than what the mere number itself conveys. We imply, among other things, that if anyone else will perform a certain operation, or series of operations of measurement, this 100 feet is what they will find. When we say that the speed of sound is 1150 feet per second, we mean that if the measurement is carried out in certain ways 1150 is the number that will be found. Even when we state that Mr. A. has found a certain measurement which he alone is capable of carrying through, what we imply is that if a certain course is adopted we shall verify that Mr. A. has found it so. So in pure mathematics also a symbol stands not merely for the number alone, but also for an injunction. Thus for 3 we say " Take three of anything " and for n " Take n of them." It was an essential step in the isolation. At first sight this may appear a trivial matter, but its importance becomes clearer as mathematical processes develop. The symbols thus really stand for operations or instructions. If, for example, we take the mark $+$ to mean "add to," then $n + m$ means a definite series of steps. It is a command to follow a particular sequence of operations. If $=$ is adopted to mean "equals," then $m + n = n + m$ is a statement that if two different operations are carried out the result will be the same. The result of the operation of addition can be isolated from the order of the individual terms. It is a compact, concise, form of the statement: "It is immaterial as far as the end result is concerned in what order any two numbers are added together." It is a mere assertion, what is called an *identity*, and anything that purports to be a "proof" that it is true is a recognition, by direct observation, that m and n and nothing more appear on both sides of the symbol $=$; or it refers back to the meaning of m and n as representing members of the system of actual numbers—isolates.

Usually when a statement such as

$$l + m + n + p + q + r + s$$
$$= s + q + n + l + r + m + p$$

is made, we verify its "truth" by direct observation, by checking that all the symbols added together on the one side appear without exception on the other. Now it is important for our discussion to realise how thoroughly isolated the statement has become. The symbols were isolated from the numbers, and they in their turn from the objects. We can apparently now verify the truth of such statements without any reference to these objects, whether they were apples or men. Our objects have now become separate letters, and they exist as marks on a sheet of paper. They move in a world of their own.

Just as the invention of a meaning to be attached to position was of such immense importance in arithmetic, so the same importance can be transferred to its more general symbolical treatment. The symbol 3, for example, we have taken to represent the operation " take three of . . ." Thus we may equally well write $3n$ to signify " take three of n." If, in particular, n were 5, this would be 5. Once more we can make statements of wide generality : " $2n$ is always an even number " or " $2n - 1$ is always an odd number." It may be regarded as a statement of what is to be meant by an even or an odd number, but if so it enables us not merely to talk of them without thinking of the elaborate series of steps from the objects of the real world from which we might otherwise derive the notion, but to recognise the way in which odd and even numbers may be constructed at will. We have effected an economy of thought and in a small way we have perfected a new instrument of discovery.

The mathematics has now become "pure." The symbols can now be used in the performance of operations that might be impossible of interpretation in the world of apples. For example, I can multiply m by n, writing it $m \times n$, or for shortness simply mn, but I cannot multiply m apples by n apples, or m apes by n apes, as an actual physical process. In becoming pure the mathematics has become free. It has thrown off some of the trammels of physical reality. This, as we can see, may become a very significant matter if we are ever to attempt to reinterpret our symbols in their final form after we have experimented with them on paper, into the real world of apples and apes. It may possibly transpire that these poor things may be shown to be something they never were, merely because the world of symbols on paper is not the world they move in. That the symbols may lead a purer and freer life is granted, but it is their own life. They have chosen to be isolated.

Let us see how these simple considerations may be set out in a form that apparently provides us with new knowledge.

Let us for example add up the odd numbers starting from 1.

One term	.	.	.	.	= 1
Two terms	$1 + 3$	.	.	.	= 4
Three ,,	$1 + 3 + 5$	.	.	.	= 9
Four ,,	$1 + 3 + 5 + 7$	.	.	= 16
Five ,,	$1 + 3 + 5 + 7 + 9$	.	= 25

On examining the numbers

$$1, 4, 9, 16, 25$$

which appear on the right, in comparison with the number of terms on the left that were added together, viz.

$$1, 2, 3, 4, 5,$$

we observe that the former set of numbers are merely those of the latter set each multiplied by itself. Thus :

$$1 \times 1 = 1, \quad 2 \times 2 = 4, \quad 3 \times 3 = 9,$$
$$4 \times 4 = 16, \quad 5 \times 5 = 25.$$

This is simply a fact of observation. There is little in it that can be dignified by the special title, mathematical reasoning. Now there are plenty of other characteristics one might notice about these numbers—for example, that they are alternately odd and even—but we have *isolated* this particular one, viz. that up to 25 this simple law of formation holds. It is a law that is *generally true about these five numbers*, and the generality has emerged with the act of isolation; we have isolated a characteristic or sub-system of this group of numbers. It is not in itself so far a *very* general law, since it is restricted to these five numbers only, but the law can be stated without mentioning these numbers individually. The process of generalisation is consequently involved in the process of isolation, and the law to be general must apply irrespective of any other characteristics the numbers may possess. *The law is the statement of the isolate.* If this is a correct statement, then it might be possible to discover a more general law that will hold for *any* number n of these terms added up from 1.

How is this to be found? By a process of reasoning?

Let us state a fact we have so far isolated merely by observation. It is, "The sum of the first 5 terms of the series of odd numbers beginning with 1 is 5×5," and let us examine this fact as the object from which an isolate may possibly be drawn, for apparently if we are to generalise we have to isolate. It is from the number 5 we have to secure isolation. Let us write our law thus:

"The sum of the first n terms of the series of odd numbers beginning with 1 is $n \times n$, where n may be 1, 2, 3, 4, 5."

Since we have to form an isolate that will be neutral to the special group 1, 2, 3, 4, 5, we ask whether it is legitimate merely to dismiss these numbers and phrase the law—

" The sum of the first n terms of the series of odd numbers beginning with 1 is $n \times n$."

This suggests itself to us as a statement of a new isolate, independent of any explicit reference to the first five terms of the series of numbers from which it has been derived. We have now therefore to find a means, if any, of examining whether an isolate of this nature is neutral to the first 5 numbers. To the pure experimenter, as we have seen, this would be handled by direct observation and test. He would, for instance, verify that the sum of the 10 numbers

$$1 + 3 + 5 + 7 + 9 + 11 + 13 + 15 + 17 + 19$$

was exactly 100, that is 10×10, and that the sum of, say, the first 25 was $25 \times 25 = 625$, and of the first 100, 10,000. He would still not be entirely satisfied, although more confident of the generality of the law. It might just be possible that at some very large number the law would no longer apply, and he must seek for some method of setting limits to its validity. The mathematician would approach the problem in an apparently different way, but, as we shall see, in a manner essentially the same. Accustomed as he is to arrange his symbols on paper just as the experimenter organises his apparatus in the laboratory so as to accentuate or isolate the object of study, he might set about it in this way.

He would write the first n terms thus :

$$1 + 3 + 5 + 7 + 9 + \quad . \quad . \quad . \quad + (2n - 1)$$

for as we have seen $2n - 1$ is an odd number, and it is the nth odd number of this series. This is what he has to sum, the numbers *increasing* by 2 at each step.

Thus the same sum would be obtained by reversing the order thus :

$$(2n - 1) + \quad . \quad . \quad . \quad + 9 + 7 + 5 + 3 + 1$$

These *diminish* by 2 at each step. If therefore he adds these two together each term to the one above it, $2n - 1$ to 1 and so on, until at the right hand end 1 is added to $2n - 1$, since the one series increases by two at each stage while the other decreases by two, the sum of these pairs of terms will always be the same, viz. :

$$(2n - 1) + 1, \text{ which is } 2n.$$

Thus *twice* the sum he is seeking will be

$$2n + 2n + \quad . \quad . \quad . \quad + 2n + 2n,$$

altogether n such terms, i.e. $2n$ times n, i.e. $2n \times n$. It follows that the sum is $n \times u$, i.e. n^2. The mathematician has established the law in its general form;

what the experimenter could only verify, the mathematician has apparently *proved*.

Now it is important for our purpose to realise that the usual mode of description of this process is to assert that whereas the experimenter proceeded by a process of testing, and verification by inspection. the mathematician has followed the *rules of logic*. Is this actually so? How are we to decide whether this is so except in the first place by actual inspection to verify the statement? The very first move in examining whether we have been guided by *rules of logic* is to test and verify the steps in the process just like a mere experimenter! If there is a logic present we must apparently observe its presence, by the method of the experimenter.

Now if we go back over the steps of this mathematical discussion, as it were with a microscope, detail by detail, from the stage at which the numbers, or symbols for the numbers, were accepted as themselves isolated, there appears to have been involved in it, apart from the verbal meaning of the symbols + or —, which are instructions to perform acts of addition or subtraction, nothing more than the simple statement that it is immaterial in what order a series of terms may be added together, and a record of the observations that all the symbols with which we are concerned have actually been present. There appear to be no mysterious rules of logic present except in so far as they are facts about the presence of marks on the paper or equivalent artificial devices verified by direct observation. If this is mathematical logic, so also, then, is the physical evidence of the experimenter physical logic, for it has an equal cogency and does not differ in kind.

By a prolonged and, to some, possibly tortuous series of tests and observations, we have, in fact, merely verified, that there is an alternative way of writing the series of injunctions

$$1 + 3 + 5 + . \quad . \quad . \quad . + 2n - 1,$$

namely $n \times n$. In mathematical language we have summed the series. We have shown that there is a short sharp command, $n \times n$, completely equivalent to the original lengthy and laborious one, and this has been produced by what is, in effect, a set of experiments with the symbols on paper.

Let us try a few other such experiments, if only to show how the subject may be extended. We have discovered that

$$1 + 3 + 5 + . \quad . \quad . \quad . + (2n - 1) = n^2.$$

There are n terms on the left, as we can see; accordingly we shall add 1 to each of these, and replace it by its equivalent, n on the right. We then have

$$2 + 4 + 6 + . \quad . \quad . \quad . + 2n = n^2 + n.$$

This gives us the sum of the even numbers from 2 up to $2n$. This again we can write, like an addition sum

$$1 + 2 + 3 + \ldots \ldots + n$$
$$1 + 2 + 3 + \ldots \ldots + n$$
$$= 2 + 4 + 6 + \ldots \ldots + 2n = n^2 + n,$$

and so we are led to observe that

$$1 + 2 + 3 + \ldots \ldots + n$$

is one half of $n^2 + n$, or as it is usually written $\frac{1}{2}(n^2 + n)$.

We have thus summed up the first n numbers. Like good experimenters, let us verify our result. If $n = 3$

$$1 + 2 + 3 = 6$$

and

$$\frac{1}{2}(n^2 + n) = \frac{1}{2}(3 \times 3 + 3) = \frac{1}{2}(9 + 3) = \frac{1}{2}(12) = 6.$$

In the space of twenty seconds we now predict that the sum of the first million numbers is

$$500,000,500,000.$$

We have travelled a long way from the original world of objects from which we derived our numbers as isolates. Instead we are moving about in a totally new universe, a flat space of mathematical symbols. All such processes have this in common, that we cannot apparently take a step, we cannot talk of the entities with which we are dealing unless at each stage we search about for characteristics of structure, groupings, and arrangements of letters and symbols that can be isolated, just as we found was actually necessary in the ordinary physical world. It may be a universe of symbols, but its operations are similar in kind to those performed by the scientist of the everyday world. The mathematician, also, must see or touch his symbols.

It has already been emphasised that the algebraic symbol, in common with the simple number and the measured quantity, can be read as an instruction to perform some operation either upon the symbols following it in its own world, or with the real objects from which it was itself an isolate. The two instructions are not of course completely independent, since the one symbolises or re resents the other. An important development in mathematical symbolism is associated with this fact.

I stand with my face to the north and my arms stretched out on both sides, right hand pointing to the east, and left to the west. Here, then, is an object or an isolate in the real world. Let us isolate from it merely its setting or position, and symbolise it in simple fashion by two lines crossing each other in the usual approved style of the compass.

To distinguish between my front and my back we shall refer to *forward* as *positive*, and to *backward* as *negative*, while to distinguish my right hand from my left we will take the *right* direction as *positive*, and the *left* as *negative*. Thus if I am at *O*, then *ON* and *OE* are positive, and *OS* and *OW* are negative. These are merely symbols, and nothing more, to represent me and my position. Whether I and my position can be neutrally isolated from my motion and all that goes by the name of me and my environment is another matter. For the moment we are merely concerned with how to represent that isolation as a symbol. An instruction is now issued to me to swing round so that I face west, my right hand pointing to the north and my left to the south. I have swung round through a right angle. Now that we have mastered the use of symbols, it is a waste of energy to continue issuing long-winded orders of this nature. Like the sergeant-major's "'Shun!" which is an instruction to brace up a complicated series of muscles, we need write merely *T*, which stands for " turn through a right angle in the way I have previously indicated." *T* is therefore an operator or an operating symbol, and, if it acts on me, it will spin me round. But the symbol for that isolate of me in my original position is the crossed compass lines, so that we may likewise let

T operate on it, and these will of course also swing round through the necessary right angle. The new E will point in the direction of the old N, and the new N in the direction of the old W. We need not stop, now that we have found an easy way to spin these crossed lines, we can repeat again. Thus

Initial position
$$W—\!\!\!\underset{S}{\overset{N}{\underset{|}{\overset{|}{\circ}}}}\!\!\!—E$$

After the one T order
$$N—\!\!\!\underset{W}{\overset{E}{\underset{|}{\overset{|}{\circ}}}}\!\!\!—S$$

After two T orders
$$E—\!\!\!\underset{N}{\overset{S}{\underset{|}{\overset{|}{\circ}}}}\!\!\!—W$$

The net effect, of course, after executing the two T orders, is that I have now completely reversed my position, the original positive direction for my hands being now along the negative side, while I am facing in the negative direction. Altogether the new position may be written as — (minus) the old position. Moreover, any line on me that was previously pointing north-east will now be pointing south-west : that is to say, exactly in the opposite direction. Unfortunately, the symbol I have used for representing my original position is still a rather clumsy picture of two crossed lines, although it is immensely simpler than myself, from which it was derived by symbolic isolation. Let us therefore merely put P to represent the original picture. All these steps and their outcome may consequently now be written in terms of these simple symbols. First P (the picture), then TP (turn the picture), then TTP (turn the turned picture). The two T's, of course, appear together because the reading is from the left and it says T is to turn the result of TP. But we have just seen that the net effect of operating with T twice in succession is merely to give $-P$ in place of P. All that we have written, therefore, may be replaced by the concise symbolism $TTP = -P$, and if we wish to study the results of combining rotations through a right angle, we can do so by studying these symbols on the paper. If T is an operator that signifies this turn through a right angle, then evidently the more complicated operator, TT, is equivalent to -1, and we now have the law for the successive application of T. Thus if the body be spun through five right angles, represented by $TTTTTP$ we know that each pair of T's is equivalent to -1, so that $TTTTTP = -TTTP = TP$, since the two negative signs neutralise each other, and the final result is merely that derived by spinning the body through one right angle. This is no doubt all very simple, but what we have to realise is that our symbol T is really of a very peculiar kind. So far when these symbols stood for numbers such as 2 or 5 or 1, or even -2, -5, -1, the operation $n \times n$, which we have written n^2, has always been a positive number, but here is a symbol such that TT, or, if we like, T^2, is a negative number. T was of course an operation, not a pure number, and its law of combination would be impossible for mere *real* numbers, as they are usually called. They were real, however, only in the sense that they could be isolates of real objects in groups; but spinning, besides membership of a crowd, is a real enough characteristic of an object.

It is an interesting illustration of the way in which isolations, once transferred to paper as symbols, are provided with an exclusive claim to being number and having reality that is denied to anything other than mere number. Because the symbol T^2 is -1 and because no "real" number could possibly be negative in such circumstances, we talk of T as being an imaginary number, and, as if to force it to wear the badge of its inferior status, we do not usually write it T, as we have done here, but i, the first letter of the word *imaginary*. Such symbols were of course not introduced into mathematics in the manner in which they have been here interpreted. They appeared rather as the outcome of statements of equality that would be impossible if the terms in them are to be restricted to simple numbers rather than operations.

What is the number x, for example, which is such that $x^2 = -1$? Clearly this is a question to which the answer is that there is no such number in the ordinary sense, but if the word *operation* be substituted for *number* in the question, it may be at once accepted as capable of sensible discussion. The apparent lack of reality vanishes.

For us this distinction, or rather this symbolic generalisation of number, is very important, since all attempts to treat the problems of the physical world, that mathematical science endeavours to elucidate, ultimately resolve themselves into handling an operational equation. An equation, which is usually regarded as a statement of equality, is, in fact, more properly to be regarded as a question. When seeking for the " explanation " of some observed phenomenon we ask by means of such an equation what series of operations will lead to this conclusion, or when seeking to make a prediction we inquire what will be the result of such and such a sequence of operations.

The next stage, then, is to attempt to explain how the symbolical processes, that seemed to have opened up a new world of thought and action and certainly a new realm of æsthetic pleasure to the pure mathematician, have turned out to be a powerful weapon for the examination of the behaviour of objects and isolates in the real world. For this purpose it is important again to realise the nature of the isolates that emerge. Science is frequently stated as being entirely a matter of measurement. This is false. The scientific movement is itself an isolate of society. It approaches the universe in which it finds itself not as a completely dissociated venture restricting itself to a fictitious world of its own creation, but as a corporate search for such aspects of the world as it is capable of neutrally isolating with the weapons of investigation it has at its command. Any such isolate is not permanently torn from its roots in the real world, but examined among other things for the limits within which it can be validly isolated. When therefore the scientist seeks to effect a measurement, he is concerned not with a mere number, a disembodied quantity, but with the measurement of a quality that persists throughout the range within which only the act of isolation is permissible. That study enables him, in setting the limits to the validity of his isolation, to point precisely to the circumstances that correspond to a change in the quality also. In stating, for example, that the presence of particles in the atmosphere may produce the effect either of a red or of a blue sky, he implies that when his studies of light absorption and scattering are sufficiently advanced he will be able to show that the presence of particles below a certain size will stop light only of short wavelength, the blue rays, and the red light of the spectrum will be transmitted. While the experimenter may concentrate merely on a measurement of the size of the actual particles and the mathematician on a mathematical treatment of the operations of the waves as they bend round or are scattered by the particles regarded as obstacles, both are, in fact, concerned with the query, " What are the limiting conditions that allow of a red or of a blue sky? "

A scientific law is thus seen to be a statement with a limited range of validity. It states a numerical relation between qualities that are capable of being isolated, and the range of its applicability extends over the range of values of these qualities for which they can be neutrally isolated. The occurrence of a new quality in a changing process is the signal for the development of a new law with a new range of applicability, or for the extension of the old law in modified or generalised form.

As far as the present discussion is concerned, the term "quality" will be taken to relate to a measureable aspect of an isolate. Length is a quality with a measure. So also is redness, or motion, when these can be legitimately isolated. A mathematician may isolate the quantity from the quality and deal merely with pointer readings as Eddington calls them, but if so, if his subject of discourse were merely the isolated symbols and the various modes of rewriting them—what the mathematician calls his theorems—he is not a mathematical physicist, not a scientist, but a pure mathematician. It would not then be his function to tell us anything about a world more real or more extended than the symbols on his sheet of paper, no matter how many of his symbols were called dimensions or space. The work of the mathematician who claims to be contributing to science is part of the scientific movement, and, while he may handle merely the numerical aspects of scientific objects, he is nevertheless concerned with the same problems as the experimenter and the layman.

The changing world makes itself evident to us by the motion of its parts, and by the alterations in position of one part with respect to the other. These two characteristics, motion and position, although they may apparently be separately isolated, are clearly interlocked. A moving body changes its location. A body apparently never changes its location without moving. That is not to say that motion and change of location are identical or that the full passage of a body from one position to another is constituted from a large number of changes in position. That is an old fallacy about which the Greeks were much concerned, and a fallacy that persists to this day. To us it suffices to recognise that motion and distance passed over are two changing qualities of an object in its environment.

Now we have already seen that the operation of turning can be expressed in a simple symbolical form. It is not difficult to show that any motion of a rigid body can be separated out into two components that may practically be dealt with individually. These correspond respectively to what is usually called a translation, i.e. a simple shift of position, and a rotation or spin of the body. A top, for instance, spins and moves forward slightly, a billiard ball or a cricket ball moves rapidly and spins. The Earth changes its position along its orbit and at the same time rotates about its axis. These two motions may usually be isolated neutrally from each other—that is to say, the change in situation from one position to another may be considered and calculated from the separate changes in forward motion and that of spin or rotation. We have already seen to some extent how a spin may be described symbolically. If we can also see how a forward motion may be expressed in this way, we shall be ready to appreciate how the general motion of a body compounded of these two motions may be dealt with in mathematical language and its numerical characteristics estimated.

Let us recognise, then, that speed, the measure of *motion*, if isolated, is not on that account independent of that other isolate, *position*. For the characteristic of motion is that its existence and duration show themselves primarily by a change in the environment—a change in position within a wider isolate. Speed and position are sub-systems of a wider environment. This is what is meant when they are stated to be relative. There is the speed of the Earth in its orbit, its change in position, regarded as part of the isolated solar system. There is the speed and position of the train on the isolated earth, and there is the speed and position of the passenger on the isolated train. As there is no absolute isolation, so there is no absolute speed.

In this sense position is given by the numerical measure of a length, and speed by the numerical measure of its rate of increase—its increase per unit of time. If, for instance, we have a short pendulum marking out beats, to which we give the name seconds, then speed is the number of units of length passed by the moving body between two consecutive beats.

The experiment of measuring the speed need not, of course, endure so long as one second. If, for instance, the speed is changing rapidly, as when a bullet strikes a sheet of metal and comes to rest in a fraction of an inch, then to obtain an accurate measure of the speed we would require the distance passed over in an exceedingly short stretch of time —short, in fact, in comparison with the total time of penetration. In all such cases, of course, we estimate the distance passed over by multiplying the speed by the time taken during the passage. Thus suppose L is the symbol for the total measure of the length left behind since the beginning, and suppose further that the length has increased by a small amount, a small difference in length, which we will write " difference in L " or for shortness dL. Suppose that the time, the number of seconds that has elapsed until the distance L was covered, is symbolised by t, then in the same way the " difference in time " during the passage across the small length dL will be dt. If we multiply the speed which we will call S by the time dt during which we suppose it has persisted, we will arrive at a measure of the length traversed, dL, i.e.

$$dL = S dt.$$

This is simply a statement of how one would calculate the exceedingly small distance dL passed over in the small interval of time dt, if the movement occurs with speed S.   Alternatively

$$S = dL \text{ divided by } dt,$$

i.e.
$$S = \frac{dL}{dt}$$

tells us how to calculate the speed if, during the time dt, a distance dL is traversed.   The smaller dL and dt are, the more closely do we narrow down the measure of the speed to a specific position.   If position and speed are separately and independently measurable to any degree of precision—and we shall see presently that this is not always so—then we may isolate from this process of calculation what would be derived in the limiting state, and say

$$S = \frac{dL}{dt}$$

where dL and dt are infinitesimally small.   If, as usual, we regard the symbols only as our isolated systems, then we may write this statement more directly by stating that the speed S is derived by the operation D on L, where D stands for " the rate of change of " in one system, and for $\frac{d}{dt}$ in the other
i.e.
$$S = DL,$$

where D represents in symbols $\frac{d}{dt}$.

The step involved in writing a single symbol D to represent the rather complicated grouping of letters $\frac{d}{dt}$ isolated from the rest of their context was a revolutionary step in mathematical symbolism. The invention of Leibniz, it meant that a single symbol, closely akin to algebraic symbols, and behaving in a manner similar to them, could henceforth represent a changing process; it was consequently a new weapon of discovery.

What we have said about the symbolic representation of the rate of change of length may be applied with nothing more than verbal changes to speed in its relation to its rate of variation, i.e., what is called acceleration. Thus acceleration is the rate of change of speed, or, written symbolically, if a stands for the measure of this acceleration

$$a = DS.$$

We have just seen, however, that

$$S = DL.$$

Thus symbolically we are entitled to write

$$a = DDL = D^2L,$$

or, in words, "the acceleration is the second rate of change of the length." It may not have been realised, but we are at this stage well into the depths of the differential calculus.

So far we have done little more than state the relation that must hold between a changing number and the numbers that must be chosen to measure it. We have phrased it in terms of length and time, but these words may clearly be replaced by any other pair of changing entities. Now the significance of what we have expounded for the problems of science may be illustrated in this way. Let us suppose a body is dropped from some point above the surface of the Earth and is allowed to fall freely, what will be its speed after, say, two seconds, and how far will it have fallen? The problem is one concerning a real body, and therefore it cannot be solved by mere mathematical symbols, that somehow do not involve a real physical fact concerning the state of motion. Mathematical symbolism, as we have already seen, when it is pure, is nothing more than the representation of the same group of symbols in a variety of ways. One such representation may be more suitable than another for some purpose, as, for example, when we found a convenient method of representing the sum of the first n numbers. If we are to be more than mere mathematicians, we must insinuate something that supplies the physics of the situation. That fact was first established by Galileo in the face of a contrary tradition that had been rooted for centuries.

Galileo discovered that all bodies, irrespective of their weight, fell to the Earth from moderate heights with the same rate of increase of speed, viz. an increase of speed every second of 32 feet per second. In our notation $a = 32$. Thus

$$DS = 32,$$

where S is the speed. This, of course, is an equation that in effect asks, " How much is S, the speed ? " From what we have already explained this may be again rewritten :

$$D^2L = 32,$$

another equation that asks what is the measure of L, the length of the distance traversed at any time ?

These are what are called differential equations, and, although enormously simplified, they are typical of the symbolical form in which all problems dealing with motion have to be represented. By this means the isolated characteristics of speed and distance traversed can be found from the observed physical fact inserted in them (in this case that discovered by Galileo) once the equations themselves as symbolical statements can be recast in such a form that from the statement

$$D^2L = 32,$$

we derive something which reads

$$L = \ldots .$$

Let us endeavour to illustrate how this might be

done.   We have already seen that speed and distance are related by the form

$$dL = S.dt$$

and of course, in the same way, acceleration and speed by

$$dS = a.dt.$$

In this case $a = 32$, so that this last statement means that during each small element of time dt there is an increase of speed of $32dt$.   The whole gain in speed during a time of t seconds is, of course, the sum of the separate little increases.   But in the symbolical form $32dt$ the only part that is changing is the dt, and its total sum amounts, of course, to t, the total time of fall.

Accordingly we are able to write

$$S = 32t$$

as a statement of the total speed after t seconds attained by a body falling from rest at the beginning of our measurement of time, viz. $t = 0$.   After 10 seconds of fall, for example, the speed will be 320 feet per second.   We have, in fact, *integrated* the equation $dS = 32dt$, as it is called, not in the orthodox fashion, it is true, but nevertheless by a process that avoids a deep knowledge of the vagaries of mathematical symbols.   Having arrived so far, we are now faced with the much more difficult task of finding L from its appropriate equation, viz.

$$dL = S.dt$$

or, since we have already discovered that $S = 32t$,
$$dL = 32t.dt$$
Once more it is necessary to realise that the total distance passed over by the body is the sum of the small elements dL at every successive part of its path. These are, as it were, the small atoms of distance out of which the total distance is derived by summation. The time of falling increases from zero when it commenced until, say, ten or twenty seconds, according to how long we propose to consider its fall. We have therefore to sum up this rather complicated series of increasing numbers $32t.dt$. What will it amount to, altogether?

Consider $t.dt$, ignoring for the moment everything else in the formula. If we can only discover what the accumulation of all the terms $t.dt$ amounts to as t increases from zero, we can obtain the total L merely by multiplying the result by 32. We can, however, make a picture of this process of summing that will assist us, the picture itself being a symbol of our symbols.

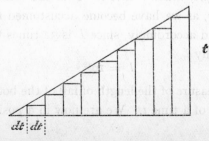

We draw a horizontal line and mark off along it a whole series of small equal bits to represent the little portions dt. Starting from the same initial point, we will draw a line which is such that at each of the terminal points of the elements dt in succession the vertical line is of length equal to the time t there. For example, after a time dt its height is dt, since that is the total time elapsed. At the end of the second interval the height is $2dt$, since that is now the total time that has elapsed, at the third point $3dt$, and so on. On this showing the sum of the large number of small portions represented by $t.dt$ is the sum of the large number of little rectangles each of which has the base dt and a height t, at that position. Thus if the elements dt be made exceedingly small, as they are presumed to become, the total value of the summation of $t.dt$ will be the area of the whole region between the line and the horizontal base. This is, of course, a triangle whose area, as is well known, is half the product of the base of total length t into the total height, which is also t. Thus the total area is $\frac{1}{2}t \times t$, or, as we have become accustomed to write it, $\frac{1}{2}t^2$, and accordingly, since L is 32 times this, we have finally :

$$L = 16t^2$$

as the measure of the length of fall of the body after the lapse of a time t. We are now in a position, in fact, to make a scientific prediction. We state that the body is dropped from rest, and we inquire how far it will have fallen after 10 seconds. The answer is

$$L = 16 \times 10 \times 10 = 1600 \text{ feet.}$$

Or we may state that the body is dropped from a height of 128 feet, and we inquire how long it will take to reach the ground. In this case $L = 128$, and we have to find t, knowing that $L = 16t^2$ in all cases.

Thus $$128 = 16t^2$$
i.e. $$t^2 \text{ is } 8,$$

and clearly the only time t that fits the circumstances is $t = 2 \cdot 8$ secs. nearly. The body will therefore reach the ground in $2 \cdot 8$ secs. from the instant of falling.

The rather detailed but necessarily incomplete study we have made of the manner in which the motion of a moving body is examined mathematically must, of course, be associated, in very much amplified form, with what has been said regarding the study of rotation. The capacity for writing in concise symbolical form formulæ which represent any complicated combination of rotational and translational motions confers on the mathematician the power of investigating widely diverse classes of natural phenomena, moving bodies such as planets and stars, moving gases such as atmospheric

E

currents, moving liquids such as tidal and wave motion. The whole of mathematical physics, with the exception of recent developments in the Quantum Theory, rests on such methods with their underlying conception of continuity in movement.

If we cast our eyes back again over the necessarily superficial development of the purer mathematics we have outlined here, certain significant features appear to stand out. What are called inductions and generalisations manifest themselves as illustrations of the method of isolation. We have, of course, done little more than indicate this. In certain cases with which we have dealt, the proof, as it might be called, that the generalisation had a wider range of validity than the isolate from which it was derived, depended, apart from the process of isolation, on nothing more than direct observation of the presence of symbols and groups of symbols, as marks on the sheet of paper. For the purposes of the more purely formal mathematical treatment, apart from any question of final interpretation of the conclusions, there appear to be involved characteristics of the individual mathematician very similar to those which the individual experimenter brings into operation in his laboratory experience. With the mathematician the verification is invariably rather more subtle. He does not simply verify a case as the experimentalist might do. He verifies a general case as if it were a particular case with particular symbols instead of particular numbers. Dealing as he does with symbols that imply isolation from the special, he does in effect see, observe, or verify that the general statements he equates in the end are merely alternative ways of writing the same thing. What are called the proofs are, I suggest, the actual steps in the process of seeing it.

If this is correct, it seems to suggest a false distinction between the particular and the general, or at any rate that we may be in danger of stressing the distinction too severely. If the process of verification of the generalisation is to convert it by a system of isolated symbolism to a verification of particular groupings of symbols, every so-called generalisation is a particular. It is, if we like, the particular case of the wider isolation, and therefore in this sense again it is valid only within the limitations that allow of the sub-isolate.

CHAPTER IV

SCIENTIFIC DETERMINISM

§ 1.

THE great vogue in the eighteenth and nineteenth centuries for the belief in a predetermined universe arose principally as a result of the continued success of the mechanical sciences. Nothing, it seemed, need be left to the caprice of mystery. Everything must yield its laws to examination. As the range of science swept out in ever-widening circles, the realm of nature showed itself increasingly subject to cogent law. True, they were laws framed by science. One does not directly perceive a law as a tangible isolate, but the behaviour encountered in the most diverse fields fell with startling directness within the same broad generalisations. With the invention of the telescope and of the spectroscope, by means of which the light emanating from stars and nebulæ was analysed, scientific law rapidly extended in range. Mathematical rules of conduct seemed universally valid, and the world stood out as a vast complicated piece of mechanism whose every cog movement could be predetermined with startling precision. Here and there slight discrepancies showed themselves, so slight in the face of the enormous mass of verifiable evidence that they were set aside for future examination when further data had been accumulated. Who wound this affair up, when it was wound up, and when it would run down, if at all, were of course speculative questions which, if accepted as legitimate queries, offered an escape for those who felt the urgent need of an anthropomorphic deity regulating the mechanism behind the scenes. When found, it was felt that he would turn out to be a magnificent, all-powerful engineer by whose original energy the machine was set going initially. At his will the grinding wheels might slow down, as they had started at his will. Alternatively he had set it running on its course, if necessary, to its own destruction.

The early pages in the history of modern mechanics began to be written in earnest about the time of Galileo (1564–1642). It was the climax of a period of physical discovery and intellectual curiosity. Simple mechanical contrivances arising directly out of the practical needs of man had gradually made it possible to explore the distant corners of the Earth and unwittingly to test, by direct experience, the ancient dogmas concerning the world about them. The globe had at last been circumnavigated (A.D. 1590, Magellan), transport and trade on sea and land had expanded, and with them had come a need for accurate astronomical data for navigational purposes. Already in 1446 books had been printed by Coster of Haarlem, so that knowledge, and with it criticism, became much more rapidly disseminated. Unconcernedly the Polish monk Copernicus (d. 1543), in a remote village, had suggested as little more than a speculation that the readings of the heavens would be most simply understood if the Earth and the planets were conceived as rotating round the sun. It seemed a trivial matter, but if accepted it meant the definite undermining of a dogma venerated as Truth throughout the centuries.

Kepler (1571–1630), a contemporary of Galileo, by an elaborate sifting of the astronomical data at his disposal, handicapped as he must have been by the mathematical crudities of the period, succeeded nevertheless in showing that on the Copernican view the motion of the Earth could be described in terms of comparatively simple laws. The Earth and the other planets could be regarded as moving practically in circles round the sun, in such a manner that the line joining them to the sun swept out equal areas in equal times : the square of the time of each revolution was proportional to the cube of the distance from the sun. Why such laws should be obeyed he could not tell. To him it was merely evidence of a marvellous mathematical uniformity and perfection in God's work. Three hundred years later Sir James Jeans rediscovered that the great Architect of the Universe was a Pure Mathematician!

Galileo turned to the world about him with the analytic eye of the scientist. His rediscovery of the principle of the pendulum—known earlier to the Arabs—that the time of swing depended on its length only, in a very definite and precise way, was one of the earliest steps in the development of Dynamics, the study of bodies in motion. It provided him with an accurate instrument for the measurement of small intervals of time, and by dissociating or isolating the *motion* from the moving *body*, in what was a fundamental problem, he placed the ladder which Newton and his contemporaries were later to mount. It is unnecessary to recount the well-known story of Galileo's oppression by an ignorant and tyrannical Church; how he disposed of the belief that heavier bodies fell to earth faster than light ones not by an appeal to ancient authority but by the physical logic of experiment, thus exposing the uniform acceleration which we call the pull of gravity on the surface of the Earth; and how he deliberately set about accentuating the delicacy of the senses by the invention of scientific apparatus. By means of the telescope that he built he discovered the phases of Venus, and verified the Copernican Theory and Kepler's Laws up to the hilt. While the prejudice of the Schoolmen and theologians prevented them from paying heed to his discoveries, and the Church watched the undermining of their authority on these matters with growing concern, the great merchant companies, realists ever, were glad indeed to avail themselves of his new optical instruments. At last his persistence became too much for Rome, and he was summoned to account for his heresies. A warning, the inclusion of his works on the Index, was, nevertheless, not sufficient to stand in the way of this propagandist of obvious truth, and at the age of seventy, after the publication of his Dialogues, Rome forced a final recantation from the great scholar. The greatest mind in Europe was in chains.

There were good historical reasons why the mighty structure that was to be supported on the framework erected during the period of Kepler and Galileo should have been built in England. Geographically isolated as she was from the Continent with its subjugation to feudal authority, she represented a suitable milieu for a speculative interest in theoretical problems. These did not emerge merely from the inner consciousness of the few scientific workers of the period. On the contrary, they were intimately bound up with the economic needs of the period. England was already the possessor of a strong and comparatively wealthy merchant class. Side by side with the expanding manufacturing processes in the country itself there was rapidly developing a corresponding external trade. Thus from the realm of industry, transport, commerce, with its inevitable military aspect, there emerged for solution new classes of mechanical problems dealing with the resistance offered to motion by boats and by cannon-balls, with the interplay of machine parts, with the position and motions of the heavenly bodies and with the measurement of tides, with the construction of instruments for observing these, and consequently with the theoretical problems of mechanics, optics, and light. It would probably be false to assert that Newton's personal motive in attacking the problems he did was due to their commercial importance. Newton (1642-1727) was a genius to whom the problems of his time were a stimulus that suggested countless isolated systems. There is little trace in his mathematical work of any such source. Before publication his work had all been highly refined, but that he was deeply interested in the engineering practice of his day we know from his correspondence.

Newton's greatest work, his *Principia*, is primarily a treatise on mathematics, on the geometry of motion, proposition succeeding proposition in a logical chain after the style of Euclid—axioms and assumptions, proof and conclusions as sharply isolated systems. Were it not for the presence of such concepts as mass and force, it might be regarded as a piece of pure mathematics. It is worth while examining critically some of his conclusions, for in fact they are the basis of much of the advance in mechanism that has been such an effective weapon in transforming the means of production during this past century or more. They deal mainly with motion and its manifestations. The phenomena of heat and various other forms of energy transformation found no place in his work. These emerged at a later date. Newton's First Law stated that *every body will continue in a state of rest or of steady motion in a straight line except in so far as it is acted on by a force*. It is offered merely as a law without physical evidence of any kind, a hypothesis. We have to remember that we are dealing here with the very beginnings of scientific analysis, an early stage in the scientific movement. We can see now that to state a proposition of this generality without indicating the experimental justification for regarding the body as a system that could be isolated from its position and motion, was to state something that need have no relevance to physical reality as we encounter it. If accepted, the law might be regarded as a test to detect the absence of a force, but unfortunately there is no method of detecting when a body is *at rest*. What experimental meaning can be attached to the term? Would a stone lying on the Moon be under the influence of no force for a person situated on that satellite and the same stone be very much affected by force when viewed from the Earth, since it then appears to be rapidly changing its motion? Of the two notions, *Force* and *At Rest*, involved in the First Law, neither is capable of definite description nor measurement. Rest is a relative term—rest in this room, on the Earth. What applies to rest applies equally to straight-line motion. As seen from the Moon such a motion will look very different from its appearance when seen from the Earth.

Similar difficulties arise also in the Second Law— *when a body is moving with accelerated speed, the force which acts on it is measured by the product of the acceleration and the mass of the body*. What is the mass of a body? Even if acceleration were an absolute measure and not relative, like speed and rest, this would merely provide us with the measure of a single quantity—the ratio of the

force to the mass. As they stand the laws are
too personal. They may be—we shall see that
they are—very useful to any one group of
observers—say those situated on the Earth—but it
is clear that they cannot have the validity in space
and time that a general law might be expected
to have. What is force? To be endowed with
scientific validity even before it is measured it must
at least be capable of general recognition. How
would a disembodied force be observed?

Difficulties such as these have driven mathematicians to seek a formulation of the Laws of
Mechanics independent of, or, as it is called, invariant to, the special situation of the observer.
That was the great achievement of Einstein, but for
that purpose it required a reorganisation of our
ordinary concepts of space and time.

How is it, then, that laws as specialised as those
of Newton, containing animistic ideas like force and
arbitrary isolated systems like absolute rest and
steady motion, have been so conspicuously successful
that no individual has given such an impetus to the
scientific movement as this man did during his life-
time? The truth is that in its application to idealised
and isolated problems drawn from Nature, the force
concept, at least, acts solely as a sort of liaison
officer. It is a mere intermediary that falls out of

the calculations as soon as we come to grips with it. We take a stone, for example, and let it drop. It falls, say, with an acceleration of 32 feet per second every second. We hang the stone on a spring balance, and the spring extends by some measurable amount. Hooke, a contemporary of Newton, formulated the law regulating the extension of elastic bodies like springs under the action of forces. His law states that the extension of the spring is proportional to the force applied. Double the force, double the stretch. Problem—the stone is attached to the spring and the whole is moving horizontally on a perfectly smooth table in the direction of its length with an acceleration of 16 feet per second every second, what is the stretch of the spring? There is no mention of force in this problem. If the acceleration is proportional to the force, and the stretch of the spring is also dependent on the force in this way, then the stretch of the spring is proportional to the acceleration. The answer therefore, half the original stretch, can be found without using the concept of force. We have made a scientific prediction. All that was required was to state Hooke's Law and Newton's Law in a form so combined that the force drops out. It is not required.

Exposing as t did a method of accurate prediction, the Newtonian system appeared to give a clear, machine-like picture of Nature as an engineer would visualise it. Although Newton was himself a highly religious man steeped in the almost mediæval mysticism of his age, he was nevertheless the creator of the first scientific system cast in a deterministic mould. Leibniz, a contemporary continental mathematician of great eminence, a co-discoverer with Newton of the differential calculus, asserted that he had robbed the Deity of some of his most vital attributes and had sapped the foundations of Natural Religion.

Newton's Law of Gravitation, coupled with the mathematical technique of the Differential Calculus, cleared the way for an all-but-complete solution of the whole mass of problems in the field of Astronomy. Once more the statement was framed in " atomistic " form, presumed to be applicable to elements of the universe dissociated or isolated from their environment. Every particle of the universe, according to his statement, attracts every other particle with a force which is inversely proportional to the square of the distance between them. Such was the famous inverse square law.

This law, again, is framed in terms of the concept of force, but if it be associated with the Second Law, as already explained, that concept may be dropped out. The statement simply implies in the language of this treatment that every particle of matter may be regarded as an isolated system, provided an environment be associated with it, such that any other particle in its neighbourhood will fall towards it with an acceleration inversely proportional to the square of the distance between them. Actual measurements of the accelerations with which masses fall towards each other have served to confirm that to a very high degree of accuracy such a state of affairs may be regarded as a legitimate isolated system. For further verification there exists a vast wealth of prediction of astronomical data derived on this assumption.

It is important to recognise with what Newton and his successors have had to deal. The changing matrix of processes which is the universe was conceptualised in terms of material particles. The implied assumption was that if such unchanging "properties" as Newton described be attached to each particle, then from a concourse of these, interacting in this purely mathematical, almost geometrical, way, the gross behaviour of matter as we in fact find it may be deduced. It is a bold assumption, and what is surprising is that, as far as the more familiar astronomical processes are concerned, it succeeds to an extraordinary degree of precision. The sole justification for

such a step is its success. The success of this
method requires an important qualification. The
verifications have almost entirely been on the
smaller astronomical scale, where matter is very
sparsely scattered in space. Sir James Jeans points
out that on a scale model in which the stars are
ships, the average ship will be well over one million
miles from its nearest neighbour. We can thus
realise how rarely they come within hailing distance.
It is now known that the law of inverse squares
cannot be valid for so-called molecular distances in
closely packed environments. It does not seem surprising that the heavenly bodies, gigantic as many
of them are with reference to our Earth, should
behave approximately as isolated systems. Actually
the Newtonian law or, as I prefer to call it, this particular method of isolation, is known to break down
at the two extremes, molecular and nebular distances.
This does not mean that the predictions already
verified have become invalidated. It merely means
that some other mode of expression is required in
these altered circumstances. If the whole scheme
could be unified, one law for all ranges, the
æsthetic sense of the scientist would be profoundly
stirred.

§ 2.

With such a record of success in predicting aspects of behaviour of gross matter it was natural that inquiry should turn to an examination of the forms of matter "inhabited by life," if only to discover how far the methods and explanations already developed could be applied to interpretation and use in medical practice. Living matter, the material we embody, has a peculiar significance for us. We cannot see our behaviour as dispassionately as we can that of a bicycle or a steam engine; we are so close to it. Anyone who has become accustomed to observe human behaviour will hear the most fantastic explanations and motives voiced by people, concerning themselves and their actions. With comparative ease we can isolate a bicycle or any part of it from its environment, and, by the very act of that isolation, subject it to analysis for purposes of prediction. *We cannot neutrally isolate ourselves from ourselves.* "Man, know thyself," is an impossible command to follow. The discovery of what isolated sub-systems we possess, if any, with respect to our environment has scarcely begun in earnest. Even in the study of other living beings we have not yet thoroughly tested the technique of handling them as we would handle an inanimate object, whatever other technique may also require to be developed in that case. A cat is held by its paws a few inches above a table and dropped. By a complicated system of twists and jerks it succeeds in falling feet foremost, and our natural inclination is to say that the cat *knows* in which position it can land with the minimum of shock, and so it adjusts itself to the appropriate posture. Such an explanation in terms of animal motives does not suggest itself to us when we are discussing how it is that a loaded dart always falls with the point downwards. In that respect we have advanced beyond Kepler, who apparently believed that the planets were urged on their courses by spiritual forces. We do not now tack on motives or spiritual urges to a dart, as we do " properties." Considering the short time, however, that has elapsed since the methods for the study of inanimate matter have been applied to living organisms, and considering the comparative complexity of the new problems, the progress in this respect has been remarkable. The early mystical belief that the material of the living body—so-called organic matter—was somehow different in kind from that of the inorganic variety, has now all but vanished. There is scarcely a product of the human factory, as the body indeed is, that cannot be reproduced in the laboratory. More and more the functioning of the detailed parts of the interior of the body, its chemistry and its dynamics, is being explained by the same methods that have been so conspicuously successful with large and small mechanisms. But man, like any other object, is not necessarily describable wholly, even as regards his outward behaviour, by the actual materials of his body that lie within his skin covering. In so far as the subject of study chosen is the " whole " body or a " whole " organ, it is essential in the first instance, as we have seen, to discover by actual experiment whether the object in question can be regarded as an isolated system, or, if not, how much or how little of its environment has to be included in the system to render it practically isolated. In other words, can constant, unchanging " properties " be attached to the organ, or to the organ and some of its environment, in order that the totality of behaviour of the whole body in any prescribed environment may be explained in terms of these? This, as we can easily see, is no simple matter. It is not even clear in the first instance that any measure of success is likely to result from it. For man is himself an element of the larger unit, society, which, including his own body, is his environment.

If, again, we were to attempt to explain the human behaviour of a changing society as the interlocking behaviours of its human elements, we should require, if it were possible at all, to attach to each human element such properties, such unchanging properties, as would enable the larger society to be a sum of these, just as we attempt to explain the total behaviour of a complex system of planets by the existence of individual planets in an environment represented by attractive forces between them. Society is a much more densely grouped collection, with an infinitely more complexly interwoven environment for each such element, than anything that has so far been encountered in planetary physics. Heavenly bodies have no social life. Even to attempt to predict the behaviour of biological man as a social animal involves therefore making a close and detailed study of society, the environment in which he reacts. As with the experimental sciences, one requires first to collect the data for the larger whole in order that the isolated systems, *if any*, that can be separated out may be examined and if possible measured. Only thus can we hope to discover how man, himself a tentative conscious isolate, behaves in their presence.

While Biology, as a separate study, seeks simple reactions to simple elementary stimuli, to be ready if possible to predict the reaction to the complex stimuli of society, Sociology at a different level must run parallel with it by analysing the structure of society and the isolates to be found in it. A knowledge of the geographical situation of a population—for example, of the material resources at its command, including its technological equipment—can assist in delimiting very broadly the structure of its possible industries, the means that have been fashioned in production, and how social strata arise. An examination of the history of society in the light of these factors may serve to indicate the general trend of the changes that are imminent in the social and industrial structure, and to throw into relief the contending forces that appear to be striving each against the other for mastery, the forces of conservative tradition as opposed to those of revolutionary discovery. Investigation of the biological make-up and of the genetic characteristics of individual stocks and of races, if carefully interpreted, may serve to set broad limitations within which mankind may possibly develop, and evolve means by which it may conceivably cleanse its population, a generation or more ahead, from features that may seem undesirable now. A study of the way in which patterns of behaviour are built up should throw light on the manner in which social institutions and social stratifications contribute to determine our individual conduct and our choices. Most important of all, they may throw into bold relief those characteristics that distinguish man from his lower stocks by showing how verbal behaviour can have originated, and with it the inquisitive traits of man. These are necessarily associated with all that we can mean by progress, invention, and social intercourse, the revolutionary influences that drive man from the static level of an ant society.

These and innumerable other factors can be recognised as possible isolated systems within the complete panorama of society. Compared with the nature of the material to which physical science usually confines itself, they can be seen to provide merely a broad, indefinite background against which we can discern still without much precision the nature of the factors that mould a changing society. To say that they represent material out of which a mathematically exact determinism of individual behaviour can be constructed at this time, or within any reasonable time, is to stretch the meaning of the word beyond legitimate bounds. From a perspective, sufficiently distant to render the detailed complexities obscure, the broad outline of the development of society may be recognised and qualitative predictions regarding the next significant change in the scene may be ventured. In that sense, and in that sense only, may we assert that there can be discerned, at least in the realm of Sociology, a form of general determinism of a historical-geographical-biological nature. Since, however, except in certain special classes of problem, there does not exist any detailed numerical technique to enable predictions to be made with exactitude, or to enable the probability of such happenings to be assessed with a definite precision, or a definite lack of precision, it seems too early to talk of detailed scientific determinism either for the isolated system that is society or for the sub-system that is man.

The exceptions to which I refer are such as can be handled by statistical methods. Within a slowly changing society, so situated productively and geographically, for example, as to be comparatively stable, isolates may be discerned and their rates of change correlated with other such changing features. Such isolates correspond to the qualities that are dealt with in natural science as measurable. If it is really legitimate to regard the whole " population," the larger isolate, as composed of isolated units or random atoms for the purpose in hand, then of course there is a field for such methods. As in all branches of science, the justification does not rest on any a priori assertion, but simply on their success as modes of prediction. That there are such possible isolates is of course clear, since slow population changes, and industrial and commercial organisation on a large scale, are actually handled by these methods, assisted by elaborate computing and sifting machines and an increasingly complex mathematical theory. It is difficult however to see how these methods can hope for any success except in fields where the changes are in no sense rapidly catastrophic. The significance of the predictions is of course related to the group or population and cannot be applied to the individual member of the group except in a very indirect way.

§ 3.

At the risk of adopting the attitude of objective idealism to which reference has been made earlier, let us now turn to a study of that part of the physical process that can be neutrally isolated from man in order to examine whether it is possible that even here there may already be signs that the deterministic method of science is likely to break down.

Following the usual scientific procedure, we must therefore decide on a critical test that will enable us to recognise when and how determinism manifests itself. Taking the world as the unified process it is, there seems at first sight nothing to deny that at any moment anything whatsoever might happen. We seem as little capable of describing what the state of the world in all its phases will be to-morrow as we are capable of recognising it to-day. The problem is too vast and complex for such an integrated treatment, but that connections exist between parts is too patent to miss. A sectional process may at the present moment be maturing in the bowels of the Earth which, reaching its climax as a vast eruption in the Andes to-morrow, may clearly obtrude itself as a factor in settling the nature of the weather conditions over the Atlantic during the following week. Dry rot may have already attacked the structure of this building so that whatever else may happen it will certainly be levelled to the ground before the lapse of some definite period. The world is full of happenings, partial processes, events we call them, systems capable of being isolated that are not obvious to us at the moment, but in the course of time they may manifest themselves in a very definite way. We may be ignorant of these things now, but they are the raw material of the scientific study of the future. To ask therefore whether the world " as a whole " is determinate is to pose a foolish question, for the material upon which an answer can be based, in a form complete enough to reply to such an all-embracing problem, is not available and can never be. To attempt to answer the question in this form would imply seeing science as a process completed instead of as one evolving, for science is itself an integral part of that changing world. If therefore we are to frame an intelligible question on this issue, it must deal with those aspects of the world about us that have already been the subject of study. If science has, in fact, found that its world is deterministic in some sense, the next step would be to discover if there is any evidence to suggest that this characteristic is not restricted only to those isolated systems which science so far has found it can treat.

How could determinism show itself in science? The process of science, as we have now seen, results in the formulation of laws of the behaviour of those things that may directly or indirectly affect the human senses. What I mean by indirectly is nothing more than that operations may occur that do not at once stimulate any of the naked senses and yet by a roundabout process may be made to do so. With the eye we cannot perceive electro-magnetic waves outside the range of the ordinary rainbow, but they may be made to affect a photographic plate if they are of very short wave-length like ultra-violet rays, or they may be made to work a loud-speaker if they are long, like wireless waves.

Laws of behaviour are always generalised statements of what has occurred in the past. They can be nothing more. They are based on past evidence and have no *guaranteed* validity for the future. In this sense there is no determinism in science or anywhere. In space likewise their validity is restricted to a region extending merely to the furthermost range of observation. If, however, without that guarantee these laws turn out to have had a validity wider than the restricted facts upon which they were based, we are entitled to state that as far as the behaviour they describe is .concerned they have manifested a determinism in the world of science. The first test we can apply, therefore, of the validity of determinism is that involved in the possibility of framing laws that provide accurate explanations and predictions of facts discovered consequent on those upon which the laws are based. To the scientific man, then, prediction, explanation, and determinism must go hand in hand. To science the test of determinism rests first on the success of its forecasts. Whatever else scientific men may say to the contrary concerning what they believe in their private capacities, as scientists they give the lie to it by proceeding on the assumption that the material that science selects fashions a determinism in the sense outlined. If we cast our eyes back over the history of physical science, three forms of prediction present themselves.

There is, first, the obvious one where it is stated in advance what will happen ten seconds or ten million years hence, with varying degrees of assurance. We mix measured quantities of common salt and sulphuric acid, raise the mixture to a definite temperature, and can state with great precision how much hydrochloric acid will be evolved after the lapse of so many minutes. On this form of prediction the whole of industrial science and technology and the whole of engineering rests. Modern civilisation and modern culture would fall to pieces if it were false. The safety of communities rests on its truth. A train, a Bradshaw, a bridge, an electric power-station, newspapers and books, wireless, and transport of every kind, all persist as evidence of it. From their experience of it human beings have developed a pattern of behaviour, a sense of personal expectation upon which they build their lives. It is ingrained in their speech. Things do not happen because we expect them. We expect them because they happen. Even the most rabid anti-determinist would lose his temper were this form of determinism not manifested at every turn. Private individuals and national Chancellors plan on it as a basis.

There is, secondly, what might be called inverse prediction into the past outside the range of experimental verification: how a certain type of rock formation occurred, how in remote ages the Earth was dragged from the atmosphere of the sun by a passing and massive star, how certain fossils have come to be where they are, or how the Earth was inhabited by certain monstrous animals at such and such an epoch. By the cumulative evidence of many such detailed predictions backward and by isolating common features of each there emerges a generalisation of the past such as the Theory of Evolution. It may be stretching the meaning of the word to use prediction in this way, but to do so unifies a common mode of deduction and induction. In this form it is scarcely distinguishable from the usual meaning of explanation. As with all predictions that are anything more than mere inspired biblical prophecies or extracts from Moore's Almanack, they are couched in the form of an explanation, but it is one which usually begins with an unverified assumption. It says in effect that *if* a star passed close to the sun in such and such circumstances the situation at present found would actually emerge. It may be the only assumption that fits the facts as known, or it may merely be the simplest. For this very reason such a form of prediction cannot have the same status as one which is based on facts now known and is again found to fit the facts as they emerge in the future. It is verified at one end of the scale only. A generalisation like the Theory of Evolution, however, while still a theory in this sense, stands rather apart in that it links together in one statement a vast mass of diverse data, each of which would stand on the footing of an individual prediction of the type falling within this category.

To the layman these are the two most important modes of scientific prophecy, in that they can be put in a form spectacular enough for the daily Press. In the third type the prediction goes back into the past, but not sufficiently far to be unverifiable by documentary evidence now. Thus it is possible to predict that a total eclipse of the sun must have occurred in the reign of Hammurabi, a prediction based on a study of the recent behaviour of the planets; and there may be historical evidence to verify the statement. It is the same process that a detective uses in reconstructing a crime, but it is literally expressed in more measured terms.

The fact that prediction has been scientifically so successful in both directions over such a vast field is, of course, nothing more than the fact that science has itself been successful in explanation. The formation of scientifically isolated systems enables the material to be handled in precise and measurable terms and to be explained with reference to these numerical relationships. It enables an accurate statement to be made of the limitations within which the isolated system can be validly separated out. The success of science and the presence of determinism are indissolubly linked up with the possibility of forming such systems. No law is acceptable unless it can stand the test of prediction, within some restricted range of validity.

§ 4.

The subject-matter of such studies as have been successful has consisted mainly in things that can be circumscribed, roughly speaking, in space and time of moderate dimensions, the world that man experiences, and as a feature of that world we cannot deny the type of predictable and therefore deterministic activity that science has exposed. The range of space and time over which this is valid is, of course, a matter for experiment, but in the attempt to extend the range there are a number of points that have to be carefully watched if we are not to fall into a fallacy that has spoilt much of the discussion on this matter. Whatever further may develop, *the form of determinism already separated out by science stands*. That rests on inescapable evidence.

The constitution of matter has been the subject

of intensive and almost feverish study during this past thirty years, ever since the discovery of radio-activity. Prior to that stage, matter had been analysed mainly by chemical methods, broken down to its chemical constituents, amounting roughly to ninety-two elements. Commencing with the isolated system *Material Object* with its gross " properties," there had been isolated from it the *Atom*, whose existence, however, as a separate object was not directly discernible. To this atom had to be attached such properties as were essential to represent in quality and in quantity the behaviour of the gross matter from which it was presumably isolated. These properties were mainly of a chemical nature, although not purely so. Such a characteristic as *rigidity* usually considered a physical property which every body displays in varying degrees, is not easily accounted for on this view. For this purpose it is usually held that the atoms of a bar of iron, for example, although free to move about to some extent in all directions, are held in just the shape of the bar, and no other, by their mutual attractions. If it should not be possible, however, to reproduce the rigidity of the bar by such a movable grouping of iron atoms, this would not affect the fact that the bar is, *in fact*, rigid. Failure to account for it in this way would merely mean that in the attempt to break down the conception of a bar to more elementary constituents, each as a system isolated from the other, we had been baulked, and some other form of isolated system must be sought. That in itself would not be remarkable, since the simple isolations requisite on the scale of the solar system where the elements of the system are scattered at vast distances apart, might have little value for the problems concerned with the congested state of an iron bar.

This practically was the situation until the onset of the radioactive discoveries. The atom was regarded as a sort of billiard ball, existing of its own right with its own properties, explaining and predicting many things, but not quite accounting for some very obvious facts. Then came the series of revolutionary discoveries that showed there could also be separated from matter tiny charges of electricity—negative and positive charges shot out with tremendous speeds. Matter then could be *broken down* into electricity. It is unnecessary for our purpose to describe the successive steps that led physicists to frame a new series of isolated sub-systems of the atom. Contained in it there is presumed to be a charge of positive electricity, a central nucleus, and embedded in that nucleus and also circulating around it at various

F

distances at enormous speeds are tiny charges of negative electricity (electrons). Now it is important to realise that this is presented as a sub-system of the atom, which is itself a sub-system of matter. Matter is what we encounter; the atom as such we do not see. Although greater optical magnification than a few thousand diameters can be easily produced, it is not profitable to do so, as no further detail is to be obtained. This arises from the fact that light itself (light energy) has a structure in the same sense, with the result that there is a limit to the smallness of anything we dare ever hope to see. We can never see directly if atoms are present by means of a microscope. The deductions from the atomic theory nevertheless have been so many and so various that the fact that they have been verified in these very large numbers of cases, and that so many predictions have been carried out on that theory, shows that the isolate is a valid one for a great variety of purposes. The kinetic theory of gases, for example, rests entirely on the assumption that a gas is composed of an enormous number of such atomic billiard balls shooting about at random in all directions. It is from the bombardment of the particles on the walls of the containing vessel that the pressure of the gas is presumed to arise. In fact it is not difficult to show that, for a *completely* isolated system, such a view does involve the ordinary pressure gas laws of Boyle and Gay-Lussac, to which we have already referred. For this purpose the mass of randomly shooting billiard balls is supposed to constitute a system isolated totally from the rest of the universe. The individual atoms are, of course, not visible, and by talking of them as if they had individual existences in this sense we may be committing a serious fallacy. A few generations of such unreflective verbal habits among scientists have accorded atoms a status of independent existence to which they may not be entitled.

Tiny particles, left in suspension in a fluid for a long time, and separated off from any vibration or other apparent disturbing influence, can be seen to be jerking about erratically when they are examined in the fluid through a powerful ultra-microscope. The smaller they are, the more lively their behaviour. The only kind of explanation that suggests itself to us is that, large as they are compared to the individual atoms or molecules of the liquid, they are being punched by collisions with these high speed billiard balls, in front, behind, and on all sides, as a fat man might be jolted and jostled about by a hurrying and scurrying crowd of larking youngsters. On this view the manner in which this jolting would show itself has been predicted and verified by actual observation. Here again is a prediction and an explanation verified at one end but resting on a theory at the other end. The evidence for the theory is, so to speak, circumstantial. In the same way, the viscosity, temperature, and energy of an isolated mass of gas have been connected with the speeds with which these atoms are shooting about and the manner in which they may spin on colliding with one another; from all this there has emerged a whole technique of gas study, thermo-dynamics, bristling with predictions and explanations, ranging from the conditions in the interior of an engine cylinder to those in the interior of a star. To meet many of the requirements of chemistry it has merely been found necessary to suppose that the atoms of different gases possessed their own invariant properties—those in fact that were shown by the substance experienced in the gross. They have been expressed in rather strange terminology for a science—" chemical affinity " they were called.

It is not clear, however, how all the gross properties of matter are to be referred back to these atomic balls without so complicating the isolate as to make it unmanageable. Why, for instance, can most solids retain any shape to which one cuts them? Wherein lies the difference between a crystalline substance, a jelly, and a liquid? To many such questions answers of sorts have been found, but as they accumulate the simple atomic isolate becomes increasingly complex.

Hope springs eternal in the scientist's breast. So he looks forward to light being thrown on these matters by the electron theory. The negative and positive discharges of electricity are, however, definitely derived from matter, and accordingly scientists have taken them as sub-systems of the atom. Like the atom, individual electrons cannot be observed or handled, but charges of electricity moving at speeds which are a considerable fraction of the velocity of light may make their influence felt in other ways. Thus there is no doubt that what we call electricity is actually derivable from matter. What precisely is the arrangement of these charges in relation to the positive nucleus is still a matter of some obscurity, but every day sees available further information on the subject. The supposition, for example, that the atom itself is a grouping of these charges lying or moving in layers at different levels from the heavy central positive nucleus within which is embedded negative charges has served to reduce the number of separate and iso-

lated properties it had previously been found essential
to fix to the atom. Thus on this view the simplest
atom appears to be that of hydrogen. It has the
lowest atomic weight. The order of the element in
a table of weights is called the atomic number.
Thus hydrogen has atomic number 1. Its nucleus
consists of a charge of one unit of electricity, and
somehow associated with it is a negative charge,
the electron, giving no total charge. The positive
particles that have been knocked out of matter
contain practically all the mass, the electron having
only about 1/1800 of their mass. The burden of
the atomic weight therefore is mostly to be thrown
on the positive centre, but it must have its electron
or it would behave like charged hydrogen. More
complicated forms of matter are to be conceived as
built up of combinations of these. Thus helium
is second in the list of atomic weights, being four
times as heavy as hydrogen. It is considered as
composed of four positive nuclei held together
internally by two negative charges. This leaves it
possible to have two remaining negative charges
circulating around outside, and the model is now
so far complete that it fulfils the more immediate
requirements of electron theory. It provides its
verifications. Thus, for example, the so-called
alpha particles that are shot out of radium are

known to be helium atoms from which presumably
two outer electrons have been stripped. Quite a
number of independent obscurities have in this way
been linked together.

The fact that atomic weights were found by experiment to be fractions instead of whole numbers can
be explained on this theory. The atomic weight
depends on the *number* of nuclei or " protons "
present, but its chemical properties primarily depend
on the nuclear *charge*, and this will vary with the
number of negative electrons associated with it. In
this way, for example, Aston has shown that there
are really several gases which we have grouped
together as chlorine with average atomic weight
35·456, but differing in certain very subtle forms
of behaviour. Mixtures of these in definite proportions previously gave us fractional values instead of whole numbers for the atomic weight.
In the same way chemical " affinities," which had
been fastened so arbitrarily on to the isolated
systems we called atoms, now appear as a consequence of the presence of the negative charges in
the outer layers of the atoms, so that there may
be regions of it through which the attractive force
of the central nucleus may penetrate and thus
establish a bond of affinity with an atom itself
suitably attired in a fringe of charges. These are

only a few of the many atomic puzzles of the past generation that can now be seen to represent mere aspects or sub-systems of the electronic isolate, and its groupings. The atom which at one stage in the development of scientific explanation, prediction, and consequent discovery was an isolate of extreme utility, for some purposes is now being displaced.

That the simple concept of an atomic planetary system obeying laws such as we have come to associate with the solar system is not an adequate isolate is clear. The fuller reality we know is matter. These are all mere sub-systems, attempted isolated systems at a level of space and time well below the range of direct visibility. In framing these sub-systems we commence by attempting to carry forward the isolations of grosser matter, to which we have become accustomed. Forgetting that the isolation of motion from matter is justifiable only in so far as it is found to work in practice, we watch in amazement the fickle electron when, discharged apparently as a charged particle from matter at an enormous speed, it impinges on a plate and suddenly loses its identity as a particle and becomes an electrical wave-system. We need not be startled. It would indeed be remarkable if the kind of isolated systems suitable for widely separated bodies remained still adaptable to these limiting forms. It is not even clear that the ordinary isolates of time and space are usefully to be applied at this extremity.

For the present discussion the significance of all this is two-fold. In the first place, the so-called peculiarities of electronic behaviour merely involve difficulties in the formation of isolates for purposes of explanation. It means that although attempts are continually being made to form sub-systems that by their combination will give rise to the type of behaviour we encounter in gross matter, suitable sub-systems have not yet been found. Since the proposed field of study is just on the borderland, indeed in many respects outside the borderland of detailed examination, it constitutes a happy hunting-ground for the mathematician. Here he can disport himself to his heart's content in the endeavour to invent such a type of sub-system as will fit the acknowledged facts regarding the electron, and at the same time by a combination of these " explain " the larger behaviour of the atom. It is no easy problem, and its solution may not be possible along the hitherto orthodox lines. For, although matter may be conceived as capable of being broken down into individual atoms with discrete unchanging properties when isolated, it does not follow that these are the properties they must exhibit when congregated together in each other's environment. Although the atom may be broken down into negative electrons and positive nuclei, it does not follow that the *invariant* properties that can be attached to individuals will necessarily suffice when these are grouped together so that they become part of each other's environment. That such complexities arise is evident from the fact that to describe the behaviour of two electrons adequately in mathematical terms requires a space-time of *seven* dimensions. Again, there is nothing mysterious in this. It does not suggest that two electrons can exist only in a space of seven dimensions. It is merely a statement of the difficulties to be faced by the mathematician in endeavouring to approach a problem that is essentially one of " breaking matter down " into electrons, the method of the experimentalist, by considering it as one of " constituting matter from " the mathematician's electrical particles. It is a difficulty that arises from the method of mathematical explanation and nothing more, but it illustrates clearly the fundamental difference in approach between the physicist and the mathematician.

The second point concerns the problem of prediction directly, and has seen much service by scientific expositors who seem anxious to explain how science gives evidence of a basic indeterminacy. It arises in this way. In mathematical physics, in order to predict, say, the motion of a planet, we require to know its position and its speed at some instant, and after that the general law governing the accelerations acting on it will enable its future position to be specified to any required degree of precision. The more accurately the initial position and the initial speed are specified, the more accurately can the prediction be made. Scientists are not philosophers or logicians, and as long as their methods are successfully verified they rarely trouble to analyse the tacit assumptions inherent in their operations. When one takes a critical view of this procedure it is clear that it relies on the possibility of isolating, as separate neutral systems, the particle, the speed, and the position. The fact that it has been possible to build up classical mechanics on this basis is evidence that this isolation has been justifiable over a wide range of practice. But the class of problem to which mathematicians have thus become accustomed is of a special type. It concerns bodies of moderate size moving at moderate speeds. For an isolated system like the electron we have to justify the neutral existence of these isolations. Thus we have to ask, for example, whether in these circumstances we are entitled to assume the continued persistence of a localised object independently of its speed.

I have already dealt with this to some extent in earlier sections. Here it suffices to state that there is ample evidence to show that for an object of the dimensions and speed of an electron there is a definite limit to the combined accuracy with which both its position and its speed at any instant may be measured. The more precisely the position is specified the less accurately can its speed be ascertained. The two, in fact, cannot be isolated as if they were neutral. This of course is ultimately a fact of experience, in the sense that it rests on experimental evidence. In this case it implies a very important qualification on the use of the mathematical method of prediction that has been so successfully used since the days of Newton. It means that if we persist in regarding the electron as a localised object in the sense in which a stone or a planet can be so regarded, no detailed prediction can be made. Every law, as we have seen, and every method of science, is a law or a method in isolation. Likewise the range of validity of the isolation sets its limits to the valid use of the method. There can be no unrestricted law of perfectly general validity other than a mere truism. Here again, then, we reach the boundaries of our present study of Nature. And so the subject must stand until an appropriate isolated sub-system is found to replace the simple electron and until an appropriate mathematical technique for handling it is developed.

This is not the first time science has had to reorganise its concepts of Time, Space, and Matter, when it found prediction breaking down. The shift in the perihelion of the planet Mercury withstood all attempts at explanation and prediction by the classical Newtonian Gravitation Law, with its sharp isolated systems of Time, Space, and Matter but the Einstein treatment, with its new forms of isolated system, forced it to yield to analysis.

§ 5.

What does this imply with regard to the subject of determinism? " So far as we have yet gone in our probing of the material universe," said Professor Eddington in a broadcast address [1] on Science and Religion, "we cannot find a particle of evidence in favour of determinism. There is no need any longer to doubt our intuition of Free Will. When from the human heart, perplexed with the mystery of existence, the cry goes up ' What is it all about ? ' it is no true answer to look only at that part of experience which comes to us through certain sensory organs and reply : ' It is about atoms and chaos : it is about a universe

[1] March 23rd, 1930.

of fiery globes rolling on to impending doom : it is about tensors and non-commutative algebra.' "

Eddington is clearly a genuine single-minded person. The atmosphere of the quotation itself breathes this. To judge from his scientific work, I should hazard a guess that one of his greatest joys is to carry through a mathematical investigation that is finally verified as physically true, to contribute his quota to the vast number of scientific predictions that have been finally verified, to determine in advance what Nature will do, to use successfully the deterministic method, and to find it valid. The material success of the scientific age is based on precisely this form of prediction, this form of large-scale determinism. No amount of further analysis can destroy this fact, and Eddington himself has spent the greater part of his scientific life in enlarging its sphere of validity. Yet in the face of these obvious facts he asserts that there is not a particle of evidence in favour of Determinism ! It is a sweeping statement, which, taken at its face value, could mean nothing less than that the whole of scientific prediction in the past has been an illusion and that the greater part of his life's work is groundless. Eddington does not of course mean this, but when we come to examine what he does mean we shall see that it is only in a very specialised and limited sense that his statement has to be understood. We have seen how the experimental scientist, restricting the field of his study from the larger universe to smaller fragments of it, has passed from matter through the conceptions of particles and atoms to electrons. We have seen how when this process is carried through the possibility of forming isolated systems in neutral environments becomes, as we would expect, more and more difficult. For at each stage in this descent we have either to ignore part of the environment, if experiment shows it can be ignored, or to fasten more *inherent* (immanent) properties on to the smaller isolated system. At these lower ranges the difficulties of finding the appropriate isolated system if it can be found at all increase in gathering intensity, for the difficulties of a sufficiently delicate experimental technique at the limits of visibility are colossal. Indeed, at a certain stage they become definitely insuperable. It is, therefore, not unnatural that the form of prediction capable of comparatively easy application to large-scale operations where isolated systems are the subject of easy study should break down at some stage. That is really all that Eddington can mean. The fact that science must meet such possibly insuperable difficulties in its process of " atomisation " is itself capable of prediction. It is a subject for scientific inquiry, and has of course been predicted. It is a state of affairs that follows from the method of forming isolates, from the nature of scientific explanation. Each such system can have no more than a limited validity. Proceeding downwards from the large to the small, as we have done, how this *impasse* is reached is clear enough.

How is it that Eddington can see in this a form of indeterminacy so fundamental in Nature that he is prepared to sweep aside all previous prediction and apparent determinism on the larger scale and assert, " We cannot find a particle of evidence in favour of Determinism "? The truth is, I think, that he approaches the problem primarily from the standpoint of mathematical explanation. He does not begin as we have done, and as the experimenter necessarily does, from the universe as he finds it, breaking it down, examining the kind of structure he will find by so doing. He is not content with a form of explanation that tells you what a thing is by stating where and how you derived it and into what it is changing. He takes the most atomised element we have been able to imagine from the successive isolated systems and regards the universe of the scientist as composed entirely of combinations of these. If atoms are the smallest entity isolated by the experimenter, he will take the electron as his starting-point. If the electron be the smallest experimentally separated system, he will if necessary commence merely with the operating symbols of non-commutative algebra. The mathematician must always begin a rung lower on the ladder, and rightly so if mathematics is to fulfil its legitimate task of suggesting new fields of exploration to the experimenter. Eddington therefore works upwards from the element to the larger aggregate, and in doing so bases his statement about the larger universe upon what can be deduced about a *fictitious* world that would be a collection of these isolated electrons. It is a passage upwards from the unknown, and therefore it is to be expected that the imaginary universe so constructed will inherit on a colossal scale all the vicious features of its infinitesimal parent. The breakdown on the smallest scale in the usual form of prediction, which to the experimenter is evidence that he has reached the limits of his possible technique, is to Eddington the starting-point from which he will now proceed to evolve a large-scale universe, his own final stage with all the attributes of indeterminism he has inserted in it.

Of course, this is the normal mathematical method of approach, and it is a method that has had a tremendous success so long as it has operated within the range of knowledge verifiable at both extremities. Its very success, however, has led some of its adherents to confuse mathematics, the mere hand-maiden of experiment, with science, the master him-self. (Cf. p. 200.) The mathematical method is admittedly an invaluable weapon of search, but the validity of its final conclusions is severely circum-scribed both by the nature of the initial assumptions and the process itself. Ascending as it does, the process must act as a checking system to examine whether, in fact, the elements, into which a larger iso-lated system has been broken down, suffice. In theory it reconstitutes the elements in order to examine how much of the larger system is thereby involved, and by direct experimental test to discover whether anything of importance has been omitted. The larger system—in this case matter—is, however, the starting-point of public reality.

Those who maintain that modern electronic theory has exposed a fundamental indeterminacy in Nature, by thus inverting the rôles of primary and secondary isolates are, of course, faced with the necessity of explaining away the determinism that has actually been established on the larger scale. To this end, it is asserted—and at present it is little more than a mere assertion—that the apparent large-scale determinism is an illusion that arises from the *fact* that all objects are composed of an enormous aggregate of small particles which statistically, on the average, act in this definite way. The difficulties into which one is led by this assertion are really colossal and have never been faced by those who profess to believe in it. A disappointed experimenter is reported as saying that the mathematician first distorts one's problem out of all possible recognition, until it is totally different, and then solves it. In the same way, from the atomistic standpoint, the problem assumes this peculiar form, How does it arise that any object in the universe we care to select holds together in just its own shape? How is it on this basis that we can walk about on solid ground without sinking through? If the approach is from the assumed basis of atomism these are indeed difficulties of the highest order, and if moreover it introduces at its foundations an uncertainty, which might be detectible with large-scale phenomena, for we only have additional assumptions to the contrary, we will require to tread warily indeed.

" There is no need any longer to doubt our intuition of Free Will " Professor Eddington concludes from his interpretation of the meaning of quantum theory, while Sir James Jeans on the same subject likewise asserts, but with slightly less assurance, " Science has no longer any unanswerable arguments to bring against our innate conviction of Free Will." It is a strange conclusion, for it has in fact scarcely the remotest connection with the grounds on which it is presumably based. No one, of course, doubts our intuition of Free Will. What one is certainly entitled to question is the grounds for that intuition, or that Free Will in this sense has any scientific meaning. The argument presumably runs somewhat as follows, although I do not think that either Professor Eddington or Sir James Jeans or any of their numerous followers in this matter have ever set it out in detail. The fact that certain aspects of electronic behaviour are not capable of prediction in detail, instead of suggesting to them that they are attempting to force a false isolate, seems to them to imply that matter in the gross or certain kinds of matter are likewise outside the pale of determinism. The brain of a human being is such a piece of matter. Coupled with this there is the undoubted fact that each individual feels and views his behaviour as if his actions were indeterminate to others (although they are usually predicted with assurance by himself). This state of affairs is presumably Free Will. It is an extraordinary medley of personal and impersonal interpretations. Professor Eddington, indeed, attempts to describe in detail exactly how the process works and where the indeterminacy enters, but I confess I have never seen the connection with electronic behaviour. " A mental decision to turn right or left," he says in his Gifford Lectures,[1] " starts one of two alternative sets of impulses along the nerves to the feet. At some brain centre the course of behaviour of certain atoms or elements of the physical world is *directly determined for them by the mental decision.*" I do not know where Professor Eddington got these extraordinary facts. I have been unable to trace them in any published record of physiological work, and none of my biological friends seems to have heard of them. I am unwilling to believe that he merely invented this, for I am sure he would strongly deprecate physiologists inventing physical and mathematical evidence merely to bolster up some personal view of their own. The elaborate scientific technique required to furnish the facts which he states so casually, about the interaction of mind and matter, could scarcely have passed into the strict field of verified scientific knowledge without someone having heard of it. The fact is, of course, that the problem of providing and developing a suitable technique for the study of human behaviour is profoundly more complex than anything that has been attempted so

[1] *The Nature of the Physical World*, p. 312.

far by physical scientists. The primary isolates have not yet been clearly and measurably selected, and any positive statement that passes beyond the mere assurance that we know little about it, is liable to be falsely construed. Moreover, what little has already been done suffices at any rate to show that the personal conviction of Free Will has little to do with the matter. If individuals " of their own Free Will, choose deliberately " to do things that are in fact predictable in advance, there is primary evidence that the personal intuition of Free Will may exist side by side with what could quite legitimately be interpreted consistently with determinism. To take the verbal behaviour of an individual and of his reading of a complex situation, many factors of which must be necessarily unknown to him, as a true index of such a matter, according it the status of a rather involved but exceedingly delicate measuring instrument, could only be valid if it could be shown that the mind in question could be regarded as an isolated system neutral to the environment it has to register. This is clearly far from being so. We cannot even yet state what constitutes the isolate and how much of the environment has to be involved with it. The arguments of science, therefore, against the " innate conviction of Free Will " are against the validity of the innate conviction as an evidential criterion, and against importing the term *Free Will* into any scientific discussion at the level of ordinary experiment and theory.

So far we have restricted ourselves almost entirely to criticism of the interpretations of a confused and mystical nature offered by others to explain the undoubted difficulties scientists encounter in their newer fields of inquiry. It is incumbent upon us, therefore, to suggest a physically more realistic mode of interpretation.

From the time of Galileo, Kepler, and Newton to the period of the French Revolution was about a century and a half. That interval saw the clarification and development of the mechanistic interpretation of natural process. On this view the basic substance of the changing universe was regarded as tiny corpuscles of matter, each existing independently and in its own right. The fact of change was referred to the separate motions of these independent particles. Each particle possessed an inherent property of inertia in virtue of which, once the particle was moving, it tended to keep on the move; once it was at rest, it was difficult to get going again. On this basis, from the " first kick-off " the particles would have begun to distribute themselves about space, spreading themselves *qua* particles to the remote corners of the universe. Nature would have manifested the true discreteness and complete unsociability of its elements by disbanding them. To account for the fact of aggregations of particles into matter, therefore, they had to be given properties that drew them together. They were thus regarded as gravitational centres exercising forces that, operating in a fixed way, perpetually prevented the particles from flying apart by their own inertia. The field within which these forces acted was an absolute space, and an even-flowing time independent of that space; space, time, material particles, force, inertia—all fixed absolute " properties " with no real sense of sociability between any two of them.

In a world in which every breath taken affects the oxygen content of the air, and therefore to that extent affects also the breath of everyone else, these conceptions of absolute freedom and independence had no basis in reality, were essentially metaphysical; and yet the working theory within which they were embedded was remarkably successful. It was not until many years later that the internal contradictions forced themselves to the fore, and could no longer be ignored.

Newton set out mathematical equations to express these ideas in deterministic form. Given the initial position and speed of any particle, its path was uniquely settled: so also was its speed at every position of its path. Since, however, the speed and position of *every* particle could never be known, the history of any one of them, while in one sense determinate, in another was simply a chapter of accidents, as it bumped into one or other of these unspecified particles. The motion of a planet, the time of revolution on its axis, the length of its year, its eclipses, and so on, were all now capable of accurate determination, provided no accident occurred; and an accident was for this purpose in reality something for which no allowance had been made in the calculation. It was not one of the *given* factors.

" Had I known the speed and position of that imminent accident," the Newtonian could always assert, " I could have told you exactly how it was going to develop." No doubt; but unfortunately every determinist scheme has to work within such a framework of accidents. Since it started with isolated entities, each possessed of its own special private properties, inalienably its very own, all carefully specified in advance, these accidents were rank unknown outsiders, and must somehow or other be excluded from this free individualist community.

Accordingly, it is not surprising to find that the keynote of the long period of experiment and theory that followed this development was the elimination of accidents, or what amounts to the same thing, the study and prediction of change under *given* conditions. Experimental technique was directed towards the setting up and maintenance of standard conditions that remained constant and intact during the experiment, and to the adoption of safeguards to ensure the exclusion, as far as possible, of accidental disturbances or " experimental error." Every theoretical study in effect began with *given* material with *given* fixed properties in a *given* initial situation, and proceeded to discuss the process through which the material would pass *in isolation*. The unforeseen, the accidents, were pressed back by the experimenter. He saw to it that nothing should enter to deflect the process from its predetermined course. He became the god who tended the machine and, being a god, he was immune. His activities in tending were not themselves processes for study. He formulated the laws for these standardised processes, he ensured that the conditions were such that his experiments were capable of repetition, and he hoped that in the outside world, where processes were far from standardised, or given, he would be able to detect just those with which he had been in intimate contact in the laboratory. He did not explicitly assert that all natural processes would be covered in this way: but, as success followed success in startling sequence, the unexpressed assertion became a conviction. Thus it was possible for Laplace to put into blunt language the philosophy of this mechanistic period :—

> " We may regard the present state of the Universe as the effect of the past and the cause of the future. An intellect which at any given moment knew all the forces that animate nature and the mutual positions of the entities that compose it, if this intellect were vast enough to submit its data to analysis, could condense into a single formula the movement of the greatest bodies in the universe and that of the lightest atom : for such an intellect nothing could be uncertain, and the future, just like the past, would be present before its eyes."

Here the Intellect stands apart. The future will be certain for It. For whom, then, will *Its* future be certain? Is it presumed that this great Intellect is endowed with the capacity to *know* the data rather than to acquire them? Can It acquire them without in some way making them, without in some way being part of the process out of which they arise? What justification can there be for supposing that this great Intellect can itself run through its process *in isolation* just like the machine constructed by the great intellect? How sensitive is It to what we have called "accidents," all those processes that the scientist has to exclude if his method has to be a simple mechanically deterministic one? Laplace may have asserted that he found the hypothesis of the existence of a Divine Being unnecessary in his analysis of the processes of Nature, but he belied his words in his practice, for in order to justify the completeness of his method it was essential for him to assume the existence of a Supreme Intellect that could understand and examine without interfering with these natural processes. This is the dilemma into which the mechanist must ultimately slip in his attempt to deal with an interrelated universe in terms of completely isolated atomistic elements.

What is the Problem?

We are concerned, then, with a much wider problem; no less than the discovery and analysis of the regularities manifested in Nature, the rational description of their relationship, and the use of these regularities for effecting further change.

Where Do We Begin?

Now, existence is always " existence in groups." This is fundamental, and must show itself at every part of any analysis of nature. It implies, however, that every process studied has to be seen as a part-process, as a constituent of a wider process from which it has been isolated in thought. In this sense the combustion of coal, for example, can be appreciated apart from and in association with the fact that it may be the coal combustion of a steam engine.

Every part-process is itself a group process, for it embraces a series of subsidiary constituent parts. For example, the functioning of the engine involves the combustion of the coal, the transformation of the water into steam, the transformation back of steam into water, the flow of the oil in the lubricating system, the friction at the bearings, and the motion of the pistons and wheels. These are not isolated, but linked together so that they emerge in the more elaborate process called " the running of the engine."

There are many other unified part and group processes also manifested in any such case. Each part of the engine and of its fuel, to which we have just referred, is the end-point of a series of social activities involving the expenditure of many forms of human labour and human skill, and these brought together in the final assembly of the parts of the engine emerge in this complex socially functioning totality, the running engine. Any part summates all that has gone to bring it into being in its present situation, and that part at the same time contributes its quota to the more complex mechanism that finally emerges.

What are Levels ?

It is convenient, therefore, at this stage to introduce the conception of levels. If we begin with any given process, we will call a wider one that embraces this a process at a higher level. On the other hand, any process that is seen to be involved in it as a constituent will be referred to as at a lower level. The terms higher and lower are therefore relative to the original process from which they have been drawn.

A simple but suggestive illustration of levels can be seen in relation to energy. Take a bird in flight, for example. Relative to ourselves some of its energy can be drawn off by dragging the bird to a standstill. This corresponds to the ordinary kinetic energy. One of its part processes is the coursing of its blood through its veins. This also represents a certain amount of kinetic energy. Its flesh and blood are warm—that is to say, its molecules are in a state of vibration and so manifest heat energy. Every molecule in the blood is itself a complex grouping of atoms, and these again are complex groupings of electrical particles, that in arrangement and movement express the sub-atomic energy. To tap each one of these levels requires a special technique in each case, and releases a layer, as it were, of the energy expressed by this process—the moving bird.

Change of Level.

Process change may involve a transformation that is equivalent to a change of level. This occurs, for example, during the disintegration of any group entity into its constituent parts, as in the smashing of a machine, or the destruction of a work of art; a chemical synthesis where a more complex substance with new characteristics is formed, or the production of a work of art from the raw material handled by the artist. The various levels of energy to which we have just referred also illustrate this. If two billiard balls of equal mass collide directly they will come to relative rest if they meet with equal relative speed: their temperature will rise in the impact. This means that their ordinary kinetic energy will be depressed to the level of heat energy, i.e. vibrational energy of the constituent particles. Again, theory suggests that at the centre of stars the temperature is so high that the atoms of hydrogen present make impact with each other with such force as to involve interpenetration with each other. The stable arrangement of the electrical sub-atomic particles is disturbed, and a new grouping takes place resulting in the new arrangement we call helium, a group of less internal energy. Accordingly, during impact energy is released in the form of radiant heat, and this compensates for the outpouring of heat energy from the star, and so maintains its temperature. These then imply changes in atomic and in energy levels.

Types of Transformation.

We can quickly summarise the general nature of the changes that occur, in terms of these ideas of levels. Take, for example, the varying configuration of the members of the Solar System. From one standpoint, the system repeats itself. The changes that occur leave the configuration one that is always recognisable as the same Solar System. Many dynamical changes are of this type. Thus we can say :

(i) Process changes may take place at one particular level involving movement from one localised region of space and time to another.

Again, the remaining illustrations we have given above are almost all cases of the passage during transformation from one level to another. The interpenetration of two atoms of hydrogen to form helium, the bursting of a bomb where the energy rises from the internal chemical energy of the explosive substance to the kinetic energy of the flying parts, the spread of typhoid from one person to another until it becomes an epidemic—these all represent what is one of the most common forms of transformation.

(ii) The development of a process out of one level into another.

This discussion has rested so far on the fundamental principle that all existence is " group-existence," and we have merely attempted to trace in general terms the type of inter-connectedness displayed by part-processes with each other. We must now turn to the actual steps that have to be taken to specify and describe these processes, for it is in this that the trap opens wide for the mechanist.

Fixing the Given Situation.

We have seen that at any level a part process has to be isolated mentally from the setting in which it occurs, and that this is a first step towards its examination. This is really equivalent to specifying it in terms of certain *given* conditions. What is given is the setting and the initial condition of the material that will undergo the process change under

G

examination. Here is the crucial step that will decide whether we shall restrict ourselves to a mechanist approach or not, for we have to remember that these so-called given conditions are not fixed and unchanging, although they are *given*. If, therefore, we contrive to fix them in some way so that they cannot change, or if we examine the theory of a situation in which they do not change, we shall in that case be dealing with an "artificial" situation, we shall be interfering with Nature. We have then to inquire whether such a method can cover all possible natural processes.

Phase Transformation.

Let us therefore inquire in the first place what happens to a process as it develops under fixed given conditions. I assert that in such circumstances the given or fixed conditions can be so maintained only for a limited phase of the process; as the situation develops, an internal process at a lower level is set in being that finally renders the given conditions physically meaningless. The lower level process becomes dominant by passing to the higher level, and a transformation occurs of the type (ii) we have already mentioned. This cannot be "proved" in any abstract way: it can be only an experimental fact, and as such can be justified by the multiplication of representative examples. But it is sufficiently clear, for instance, that if heat is continually applied or continually withdrawn from a substance under given conditions a drastic change in the situation must finally ensue. The same is true if any structure is subjected under given constraints to a continually increasing externally applied force. In all these cases internal stresses or internal agitational energy of the elements of the material finally force a change in phase no matter what the given fixed conditions. Physical and chemical science abounds with just such cases of phase change, or change of state, critical collapse, or instabilities as they are variously called according to circumstances. It is unnecessary here to illustrate what is a commonplace. What is important to realise is that they are all illustrations of the same general principle, viz. that the intensification of a *given* factor within a given fixed setting arouses an internal process at a lower level (growth of internal energy), and this internal process then becomes the dominating factor in the final transformation to a new phase.

Limitation of Scientific Laws.

It is the function of physical science to express in measurable form the changes that occur within any one phase. Its findings apply measurably to phases that are delimited by the break-up of the given conditions, and these phases, and therefore these descriptions, are isolated and detached from each other. We do not use the same formal law to express the evolution of heat in a wire through which an electric current is passing, over the two phases that are separated by the fusing of the wire. The given conditions break up with the melting of the wire.

To link up two succeeding phases we describe in qualitative form the critical situation that corresponds to the change in phase, and then restate the new given conditions for the commencement of the new phase. Quantitatively described, phases are alternated with qualitative descriptions of phase change.

A Query.

Is it conceivable, we may ask, that phase changes of this nature may occur continuously so that it is impossible to examine them by fixing given conditions and maintaining these intact while a part process develops? We shall see in a moment that this is precisely what does occur, and that in these circumstances the method of mechanical isolation is simply inoperative. Before turning to this, however, there is yet another characteristic of this examination in phases that deserves attention. It will help to answer the question we have just posed.

Repetitiveness in Experiments.

As long as the examination is conducted *within* a phase, so that the limiting critical points where entry is made into the next phase are not over-stepped, *the process may be made repetitive.* By relaxing the intensifying factor the medium may be led back to the same initial given conditions. If a strut is subjected to a lengthwise force while it is held rigidly in supports at the ends, it will bend under the influence of this force; but if the latter is relaxed the strut will straighten out again. Only when the force exceeds a certain critical amount, and the strut buckles and cracks, will it be impossible to repeat the experiment on the same material. It will have undergone a final change in phase. Holding the ends rigidly in supports and applying an increasing longitudinal force have then become physically meaningless.

The Significance of Numerical Prediction.

When we come to examine it, of course, it is precisely this characteristic of repetitiveness that is crucial for the statement of laws in a form that admits of numerical prediction. If we could not depend on the given conditions being also those for repetitiveness, we could not depend on the numerical predictions.

Arising out of this there is one more point to which we must direct attention. If all given conditions must eventually lead to a change in phase as the process develops, is it possible that conversely any given process involves changes in phase for some unspecified conditions? What we are asking is whether it is not a fact that every process, even when it is one within a phase, involves fundamental transformations of the type (ii) we have discussed. I take an illustration at random to indicate that this is so. Take the case of a candle burning steadily within a given atmosphere of oxygen. The phase will extend until the quantity of oxygen in the atmosphere is reduced to a certain critically small amount. The burning depends on transformations in detail of the type (ii) taking place within the elementary particles that make up the candle, in association with the oxygen of the air. The steadiness of the flame again depends on the fact that small particles of carbon achieve a stage of luminescence during the short period while they are passing upwards from near the wick to a certain distance from that point, after which they enter the cooler atmosphere and lose their incandescence.

The flame is statistically steady. It is like a fila-ment lamp that is heated to incandescence by alternating current. These continual changes of phase by the elements do not prevent the whole phase of the candle from being examined as one under standard and steady condition. Indeed, they make it possible. In a changing world steady con-ditions can be steady only in a statistical sense.

Transformation of Properties.

If this is true, however, for such a simple case, is it not in fact equally true for other characteristics that we are prone in scientific circles to regard as fixed and unchanging? What, for example, of the properties of substances, the properties of the hydrogen atom—indeed, the very atom itself? Must they not also be regarded as statistically con-stant entities? Is it also not true for " field " properties, where we attempt to fix the property on to the environment rather than on to the object itself? Science, whatever else it is, is the search for regularities in Nature, and regularities are essen-tially of a statistical nature. That does not detract at all from their reality; it merely clarifies our view of them. It enables us also to see the inner significance of what the experimentalist is doing when he endeavours to study Nature by the fixing of standard conditions, by the making of repetitive conditions, and what the mathematical theorist is doing when he postulates given entities with given properties in given situations.

From the point of view of this approach a property is a mutual relation of statistical levels, i.e. of part process to part process or of part process to that of wider group. It follows that we may expect such properties themselves to undergo fundamental transformations in phase in a changing process. From this point of view, therefore, there is nothing alarming in the idea that a statistical entity called the electron may at one level in a process manifest characteristics like those of particles, and as the process develops, or at another level, manifest statistical wave-like characteristics. Only those who insist on the unique identity and fixedness of properties will find themselves in difficulties, but in doing so they will merely betray the internal contradiction in their own outlook.

We have raised one query to which we must now return. In our analysis we were led to inquire whether it was possible that processes might exist that were intrinsically incapable of being examined in all their manifestations by the fixing of given conditions and by concentration on single phases. Such processes would therefore be non-repetitive;

it would be impossible to bring the material back to the original situation with the same given fixed conditions, no matter how small the phase. These evidently include processes that fall under the general heading of " learning from experience." If the elephant never forgets, it cannot be made to retrace the same steps in learning. Every element learned demands a new starting-point. This does not mean that there are aspects of the problem that cannot be studied by the normal scientific method, but rather that certain aspects only of that method can be so studied. This is achieved by deliberately setting up standard conditions of a statistical nature. Instead of studying the continuous process on the one individual, discovering thereby the mutual interaction of individual and environment, successive groups are put through the testing process, and the standard conditions are statistically preserved. Thus there is excluded the socially significant problem of interplay of man and his environment, in which both simultaneously are cause and effect. Excluded also are the critical stages in such an interconnected relationship, when a new unified joint process emerges at a new level. To deal with these, scientific method has itself to be transformed, attention, in the first instance, diverted away from the search for constant numerical measurements and turned to the qualitative features of change manifested by conscious human groups— sources of social energy. This means that prediction and determinism have to be re-interpreted in this human context, and applied not to phases that are reproducible or repetitive, but to successive phases that display a pattern of group behaviour. It is not possible to develop this line of approach very much further within the scope of the present chapter. We have endeavoured merely to sketch the standpoint that must be adopted by scientific men if they are to ensure that in their interpretation of natural phenomena they will be able to emancipate themselves from the mental bonds that past theory has made for them. We can now look back, however, on the mechanistic assumptions of Laplace and detect precisely where the limitations lie. In doing so it will also become apparent how much of it is still left in a confused and unsophisticated form among scientists to-day.

A mechanist is an atomist. He ignores the existence of levels, the passage during transformation from one level to another, the statistical nature of the entities with which he deals. He isolates fixed unchanging elements in the universe with fixed unchanging properties, operating in fixed given circumstances. Properties at a higher level must " emerge " in a mysterious way from those at the lower. Conscious matter must be a mystery to him. For him accidents cannot happen, because with his assumptions he must know all. He will therefore be perplexed at the inability to penetrate in detail into sub-atomic processes. He regards a group as nothing more than the simple additive sum of its constituent elementary particles. He will assume that it is always possible to study any process in all its manifestations by isolating given conditions that remain intact throughout a complete phase. The repetition of the fixed conditions will for him involve the repetition of the process during that phase. Thus, learning from experience a process that is non-repetitively performed, one in which the properties of the medium are in a continual state of change and of transformation, will be excluded from the natural processes that fall within his purview. He will thus be involved in a denial of a pivotal concept of scientific method and therefore show a flagrant contradiction in his approach to Nature. It follows that to the mechanist—since learning from experience also involves actively changing the environment—the problem of how the world is changed and how to change the world involves an inscrutable mystery. Thus one of the principal problems with which we are necessarily concerned—viz. the rational appreciation of natural process and the changing relation of this rational process to human activities— must fall outside the scope of his explanation, his study, and his activity.

The ease with which scientific men slip into the fallacy of mechanistic explanation arises from the fact that there are whole classes of phenomena for which the method of isolation provides a very close approximation to actuality. Experimental technique is deliberately designed to accentuate this isolation, and mathematical formulation explicitly assumes its existence. Because both approaches have been extraordinarily fertile in their elucidation of special classes of problem, scientific men have " learned from experience " the value of this method of approach. Those who adhere to a mechanistic form of explanation, believing that thereby they are remaining truly scientific, have not been scientific enough to appreciate the limitations of a fixed and unchanging method of approach. They assume that the scientific method has fixed and unalterable properties; and ignore the fact that as the scope of the material that scientists find themselves compelled to treat widens, so also must scientific method acquire new properties and develop new modes of approach. It must transform itself.

CHAPTER V

SCIENCE—A SOCIAL VENTURE

§ 1.

Science is a human effort. Its birth dates from the dawn of society, and it will die at its setting. Its foci of interest, as its history strongly suggests, are deeply set in the changing physical and intellectual needs of mankind. Thus the broad outline of scientific progress is sketched for it by the society from which it emerges and the universe within which it exists. If we regard the vast stretches of space and time during which universes have passed through their phases, we can recognise how trivial are the effects of man's intrusion on the scene. Like the astronomer, he is almost a mere spectator.

Yet, while he can no more control his own tiny world in all its detail than he can stay the receding nebulæ, the story of science, in a much more intimate sense, is his own special creation. It is the work of man. It is the story of his struggles with Nature. They are his formulas, his laws, his practice. The changing universe may be a datum imposed upon him, but the applications and the descriptions are man's. While the broad subject-matter is therefore not, in that sense, of his choosing, in certain ways his person intrudes itself on the scene by the particular selection of the material that is made in forming his isolates, and by the manner in which he exhibits their relations in his laws. To say this is to assert that man and science, separately isolates of the wider universe, are not, in fact, isolated from each other. He worms his own way through life and produces science. The considered statements of men of science at any epoch may therefore be expected to embody within their scheme signs that man, the historic being, has himself been at work on it. As the movement has expanded, however, so there has grown with it a recognition of the necessity for the elimination of personal, animistic, and introspective features in all their manifestations from the bodywork of science.

But man is a social animal, not a simple, self-contained machine. He must communicate with his fellow-men. Whatever else he may inherit from his parents genetically, he acquires a vast complex of habits, verbal and intellectual behaviour from society, and in particular from that section of society in which he has spent his most impressionable years.

The dominating minds of a period may help to focus the attention of the scientific movement upon special classes of problem, and thus stimulate an intensive search in particular directions. A Newton or an Einstein may plough a furrow that will be feverishly examined in detail by his mass of followers in succeeding generations, but in the end the highly specialised and technical developments will be interpreted, not to the scientific movement alone, but to its parent, society, and that interpretation will inevitably be coloured by the ideology of the class that has stirred the expositors most deeply. The influence may be largely unconscious, but that it is present no one could reasonably deny.

The scientific movement, therefore, has two sides to it. Each merits examination. As men of science individuals are interested in the one, as members of society in the other. The one has involved an organised study of the forces of Nature, the development of an elaborate technique of experimentation and explanation which would win the assent of others to conclusions by the fact that they conform to practice. The possibility of this conformity to practice, and thereby compelling assent, is one of the essential features of the scientific movement. The other aspect implies a recognition of science as an outgrowth of society, and requires interpretation in that sense. Whereas the tendency in the first is to eliminate all features that depend on an ethical or an individual bias from its categories, the second cannot escape this. As long as society is socially and ideologically stratified, the tacit assumptions of its classes will be rooted in different soils; the repercussions of science will be important here intellectually and there economically, and the sociological and philosophical interpretations will arouse controversy rather than assent.

Let us examine these two aspects of science in detail. The first deals with the internal relations of the scientific movement—its isolates; the second with its external relations, its connections, and its roots in society of which it is an isolate. The first aspect is consequently concerned with the internal features of science in the restricted sense, the second with its sociological properties.

§ 2.

The field of science in the internal sense is delimited by that region within which its devotees cannot agree to differ regarding its practical outcome. For a study of the history of science seems to point unhesitatingly to the fact that where progress has been possible it has depended largely on this characteristic of the field of study and of the workers in that field. As the scope of the movement has developed, as it has passed from astrology and witchcraft through dogma, social habit, and rule of thumb to precise experiment, there have gradually emerged with ripening experience more definite criteria of what may legitimately fall within the field of scientific study.

Any such criterion of truth may not be one that commends itself to the professional philosopher. It may be that science ignores subtleties that appear vital to academic philosophy, that it skims easily over the surface of reality. The very principle that scientists must leave no differences behind may narrow the range to superficial agreement, and restrict the nature and number of the isolates it may form. Whether or not this be so, science can at any rate look upon itself as a united movement that has left in its wake a body of tested knowledge, while philosophy is still broken up into disunited schools of thought. In spite of the unanimity that scientists exhibit in the practice of their work, they nevertheless express a peculiar paradox. This shows itself in the disagreement to be found among them concerning the internal function of science itself, and the nature of the truth it reveals. Let me quote from a few contemporary scientific writers.

" Our problem," according to Professor A. N.

Whitehead, " is to fit the world to our perceptions and not our perceptions to the world." Here Whitehead adopts the idealist position. His own perceptions are to him the prime reality and the world is a system fabricated to fit them. But whereas " a chair is a common-sense notion, molecules and electrons explain our vision of chairs." To Whitehead, therefore, the scientific scheme is a mode of explanation of his sense perceptions. The independent mind sets out relations between them, and that activity is science.

To Sir Arthur Eddington, on the other hand, " Science aims at constructing a world that shall be *symbolic* of the world of common-place experience." He does not consistently hold this view. He begins his *Nature of the Physical World* by drawing a distinction between the table familiar to him in everyday experience on the one hand, what Professor Whitehead would call the common-sense notion table—the table he writes on—and in contra-distinction to this his scientific table whose vast emptiness is sparsely scattered with numerous electrons rushing about at great speeds, and " whose combined bulk amounts to less than a millionth part of the *table itself*." Quite inconsistently, in spite of the " table itself," he adds later on, " Modern physics has by delicate test and remorseless logic assured me that my second

scientific table is the only one that is *really* there,"
although what delicate tests these can be that involve
the "thereness" of the scientific table without involving also the same "thereness" of the familiar
table and of the testing apparatus he does not state.
I doubt even whether these discriminating tests
exist. To conceive the *symbolic* scientific table as
in these circumstances more real than the table of
which it is the merest collection of mathematical
symbols is a feat of the imagination that requires
a brand new definition of reality to perform.

According to Mr. Bertrand Russell, on the other
hand, "The aim of physics, consciously or unconsciously, has always been to discover what we
may call the causal skeleton of the world." Elsewhere he says, "It is obvious that a man who can
see knows things that a blind man cannot know;
but a blind man can know the whole of physics.
Thus the knowledge that other men have and he has
not is not part of physics." (*The Analysis of
Matter*, pp. 391 and 389.) If the knowledge that
seeing people have is knowledge of the world of
reality, and if it be true that a blind man may
know the whole of physics, it seems evident that
science cannot span the whole range of reality. It
seems relevant to inquire, not whether sight can be
dispensed with and yet leave the individual capable

of knowing the whole of science, but which senses, if any, are essential for this purpose. If one sense at least is required for an individual to make contact with the world of reality, on what evidence can a distinction be drawn for this purpose between one sense and another? What Mr. Russell actually implies is that the scientific picture can be isolated from the world of sight, and that nothing that it offers is thereby lost. This is surely an unsubstantiated assertion. The statement that there is a line in the spectrum of the sun corresponding to a wave-length of 1/59,000,000 centimetres, for example, as it would be stated and understood by a blind man who had never experienced the colours of the spectrum but who appreciates the meaning of number and measurement, is vastly different from the statement that the *orange* part of the spectrum is traversed by a line of this wave-length. There is a common element in the two statements, the numerical characteristic, but the latter tells us something about a feature of the world that is absent from the former. What in fact Mr. Russell has done has been to ignore the terms " of the world " in his description of the aim of physics " to discover the causal skeleton of the world." If such a bony structure is exposed, it is not a mere disembodied skeleton, but an essential part of the make-up of the world, and cannot be isolated from it without loss.

Three other statements of the objects of science may be quoted. In his *Grammar of Science*, Professor Karl Pearson has stated that "the classification of facts, the recognition of their sequence and relative significance, is the function of science," while the scientific attitude is shown in "the habit of forming a judgment on these facts unbiased by personal feeling." "The scientific man," he says elsewhere, "has to strive at self-elimination in his judgments." In the same vein Dr. Dingle asserts in his *Science and Human Experience* that science is the "recording, augmentation, and rational correlation of those elements of our experience which are actually or potentially common to all normal people," and he goes on to amplify the meaning of his terms. "The object of all science," Professor Einstein states in *The Meaning of Relativity*, "whether natural science or psychology, is to co-ordinate our experiences and to bring them into a logical system." These are the dicta of men of science, theorists and practitioners alike. We may compare with them the point of view of a writer like J. W. N. Sullivan, who derived æsthetic inspiration from music and mathematics. "The ideal aim of science," said that writer in *The Bases of Modern*

Science, " is to give a complete mathematical description of phenomena in terms of the fewest principles and entities " (p. 22). Then again (p. 226) : " The present tendency of physics is towards describing the universe in terms of mathematical relations between unimaginable entities."

On this view, mathematics is not merely a weapon of discovery, but for science actually a necessary language of description in terms of which everything that claims that title must ultimately be expressed. There could be no purely experimental science. No matter how closely linked the ideas are, even if the causal relationships that Mr. Bertrand Russell regards as essential were exposed in succession directly to the senses by the most cunning of experiments, there would be no ideal science until it had all been expressed in mathematical form. On this showing that genius of an experimenter, Lord Rutherford, who has done so much to lay bare the inner structure of matter, can never hope to rank as a scientist. He must be content to await the coming of the mathematician before his findings can really be incorporated within any scheme that calls itself science; but unimaginable entities may be introduced. For Sullivan, the mathematician was thus finally the only true scientist. The others are his handmaidens.

In the face of these quotations it can hardly be contended that science regarded as an object of internal study has yet evoked from scientists, mathematicians, philosophers, or writers the consensus of judgment that they are agreed is a necessary feature of its subject-matter. Here are seven writers who in setting out the aim of science stress in turn the symbolic nature of its findings, the mathematical and measurable form of its statements, the causal linkages in its structure, the logical grouping of experience, and the absence of the personal element. Is it possible that all these are, in fact, necessary elements in science, and that in the absence of any one of them there would be no science?

§ 3.

How can one discover what is the object of scientific inquiry? Science is not an individual, stating in advance what he proposes doing, and possibly ignorant of what history will decide were, in fact, his objects. *There are no objects to science, there are results.* There are the vast changes it has effected in production and in social life. There is an achievement in the form of a body of agreed knowledge, and there are accepted modes of demonstrating the " truth " of that knowledge. These modes expand with the body of knowledge. Scientific truth, the process of acquiring scientific knowledge, the method of verification, and the nature of the criteria that are admissible are all interlocked concepts, and any attempt to separate the one from the other may lead to nothing but confusion. They may, however, be considered as a group, as the expression of the social movement we call science. There is no unique starting-point, and there is no unique route in its analysis. Science has emerged from man's struggle with Nature and has become a social habit, a custom; but it is a custom so geared with the world about us that it must run smoothly, irrespective of climate, nationality, or race.

In an arbitrary fashion, let us, then, consider some of the characteristics that science has exhibited, but let us realise from the beginning that they cannot be closely adhered to irrespective of circumstances— they cannot be final. For science is a growing movement, not a set of hard and fast rules.

Like the average, sensual man, its adherents accept the evidence of their senses for their common-sense world, but they take a rather sophisticated view of their sensory evidence. A single sense may easily be deceived. The eye cannot see a breeze that the sense of touch may detect. All the senses may be deceived. A suspended magnet may detect a wireless wave that leaves every organ unaffected. The magnet, the telescope, the microscope, and the spectroscope become thus extended eyes; and so with the other senses. Scientific instruments are all feelers magnifying the range and sensitiveness of our organs to a pitch scarcely suspected by the layman. However much they are refined, in the last resort the senses must come into play. The eye must be placed to the microscope and the ear to the microphone, and so the senses may still be deceived. What second line of defence has science then against error? It places the senses themselves among the objects for study in its common-sense universe.

Science states, then, that a tomato is red, a leaf is green, a stone rough, a noise loud, a molten mass hot, and it proceeds to ask questions. It is significant that the early minute-books of most scientific societies are full of inquiries whether certain questions are sensible, for the form and nature of a question usually direct the form of answer that may be forthcoming, and that answer stimulates the next line of inquiry. Does a tomato always appear red? What will be its colour in blue light? In what other respects does a loud noise differ from a soft one? How can one compare their relative loudness? How rough is this stone and how hot is this molten metal?

All these queries, be it noticed, are in the first

instance questions about isolates, and the whole trend of the questions is to emphasise the isolation from the individual questioner. If we can only get together, it seems to say, and talk about these matters as if they belonged to none of us, as if they were isolated from us, we may be able to acquire some knowledge, we may be able to find a form of impersonal statement to which we can all assent in common. The subject of discourse will be those matters that are capable of being isolated, not merely from the world outside us, so to speak, but isolated from us individually. That this form of isolation is essential to science at its present stage is evident when we contrast the queries: Is this daffodil yellow? How yellow is this daffodil? Is this daffodil beautiful? How beautiful is this daffodil? We need not be sophisticated scientists to recognise that agreement could probably be reached on the first two points, crudely as they are stated in the scientific sense. As regards the third point, verbal unanimity might even be secured. There might, in fact, be as much unanimity as with the query, Is this daffodil yellow? On the last point, however, we would be completely at sea. How could beauty be measured? The set of numbers I might produce to represent my reactions to beauty would probably appear quite arbitrary to someone else. It seems to be something personal as between myself and the object of beauty, and to attempt to isolate me neutrally from it, to attempt to regard the object as possessing an inherent beauty, in the way we might regard it as having an inherent shape or temperature, can lead to nothing but confusion. In that sense there is no isolated system *daffodil* apart from me. I and it are one in its beauty, and the scientific method of isolation cuts it out of the scheme of discourse.

At first sight, closely akin to this difficulty of beauty, is the matter of colour. A tomato is red; so much we are agreed, but it is a redness associated with everyday experience in white light. The passage from daylight to blue light leaves its shape and its weight unaltered, but alters its colour. It has become black. Has the tomato, then, a shape and a weight but not a colour *of its own*? If this were as far as we could get, colour also would be incapable of neutral isolation. In such varying circumstances the query is pushed further back in such a form as to expose a neutral feature, a permanency, an isolate that does not change, but such that diverse aspects of this unvarying property are observed. We ask, in fact: What has it of its own that appears red in white light and black in blue light? The form of the query suggests that we examine the object in detail for further isolated systems that may have escaped notice—the detailed nature of the skin, for example.

These have mainly been preliminary queries searching out a suitable subject of study. The next stage is associated with the consideration of " How much? " inquiring whether certain things are measurable and how they are to be measured. The means of measurements, at first sight at any rate, are simple in science. A quality capable of being isolated is measured by means of an agreed standard unit of that quality. It measures length with a standard rule, time with a standard clock, motion against the standard speed of the hands of a watch, brightness against a standard lamp.

A quality that cannot be isolated in this way is not one that is capable of numerical study by scientific methods. There is no unit of beauty for a musical note, but there is actually a unit of loudness and of pitch. Many of these units are themselves capable of being broken down, as far as the practical measurable quality is concerned, into simpler subsystems, sometimes depending on a theory of their constitution. Thus we need not measure motion directly against a unit speed, for it suffices to measure length and time, and the measure of motion may be estimated.

The apparent simplicity of such measurement in

science is superficial. We gain the impression that sizes, for example, are measured by placing a rod alongside the object to be measured. How, then, do we carry through the operation for measuring the size of the electron which is too small to be visible, and the distance of a star so far off that it cannot be seen with the naked eye? The fact is that most measurement is indirect. Only for objects roughly about our own size could the measurement be directly performed, and not even always then. Resort is inevitably made to calculation based on some theory of the nature of the changes that are occurring. All such measurements are therefore ultimately predictions, but so fertile have these predictions been in suggesting indirect modes of verification by extended sensory apparatus, that it is at this stage almost impossible to disentangle observed fact from theory. A theory without a prediction is of little importance in science. A prediction suggests a new field of scientific observation, and the verification is naturally expressed by the experimenter in terms of the mathematical entities of the theory. In this way has the language of experimental science become honeycombed with the language of mathematics, until it has become not uncommon for the experimenter to assert that what he observes is the equivalent theoretical isolate. Returning, then, to the previous question we find that the first steps in scientific inquiry are directed to exposing some invariant property underlying an apparently variable and chameleon-like characteristic, while the second are concerned with the query how much?

In all cases, the questions concern entities that are part of the world of common-sense reality. We are dealing with a common-sense tomato. It is common sense that it is red. It appears black in a blue light. One requires only to look at it in a blue light to see that it is common sense that it is black. Common sense, then, asks the question, Has it really a colour of its own? and the answer will not be satisfactory until common sense agrees that it has or it has not. The appeal at the beginning, throughout the argument, throughout the changes in environment, throughout the experiment is always to common sense. It is a curious fact that these last few years have seen a continuous attempt at mystification in scientific explanation by the suggestion that science has departed from this fundamental criterion. In one sense there is nothing, there can be nothing, in science that violates common sense. The fact is that all new knowledge violates the common sense of the ignorant, but it has not become knowledge without being subjected to the common sense of the initiated. Common sense among the multitude is common practice, and takes just as long to expand as new knowledge takes to be assimilated. Science begins and ends with common sense. Its knowledge is essentially democratic. It cannot remain for ever the privilege of any special class. It can be adopted by any culture, class or creed. So much at any rate has emerged from its history and its method.

" The scientific man," says Karl Pearson, " has to strive for self-elimination in his judgments." If this be a correct interpretation of the common-sense feature we have stressed, it suggests that the ideal of scientific knowledge is to reach a system capable of being isolated from the subjective world of every individual member of the human race. It would be a set of statements acceptable to all, but capable of being personally interpreted in such a way that, as far as outward behaviour is exhibited, no differences in interpretation can be detected. The formulations of science, internally isolated, are statements *invariant with respect to the individual.* Not merely is this the case for scientific facts as between individual and individual, but it has a validity very much wider than this. The whole development of Relativity associated with the name of Einstein springs from the same *motif.* Prior to the advent of his theory, the laws of science were in the main valid merely for individuals within one framework, the assumption being that that framework was "at rest" or in steady motion. No scientific meaning could be placed on this phrase, for there was no method that could be used to verify that this fictitious isolated state was indeed neutral. It was as the climax to a concentrated search for the absolute motion of the Earth through an hypothetical Ether, supposedly at absolute rest, that it was discovered that the measured speed of light did not vary with the circumstances of measurement. If the light was that emanating from a star, then the measured speed was the same whether the Earth, and therefore the observer, was moving to meet the beam or away from it—a totally new experience in science, as it would be a strange phenomenon in every-day life. In both circumstances the relative speed was the same. The speed of light was invariant to all the observers, no matter what their motion in space appeared to be. Here was a truly invariant law, neutral to space and in time and with respect to individuals. Derived as it had been from a wider field of experience this constancy of the velocity of light was a fact with a wider validity than any previously known. It opened up a field of study hitherto immune from common sense, but one which has involved a drastic change in outlook for the new common sense. This startling discovery, first made by Michelson and Morley, has involved a reconsideration of our earlier isolations of space and time as separate neutral systems. In itself it was a revolutionary change acclaimed as a violation of common sense, but it is only so to the extent that common experience of the common man rather than of the specialist has not yet found the need for a more extended space within which to accommodate the physical universe.

§ 4.

Some of the implications of the attitude to which pure science, so-called, commits itself in accepting within its framework only those statements of experience that can be formulated in this impersonal way have been discussed by Lancelot Hogben in his *Nature of Living Matter*. As a biologist, Professor Hogben is vitally concerned with man as a subject of biological study, and with man's reactions to his environment. To him Science is itself such a reaction, and one profoundly affected by the capacity of his sense organs to register sense impressions. He seeks to underline the distinction between what he calls *public knowledge* and *private belief* or sentiment. Statements we make about the world gener-

H

ally involve both a private and a public component. The public component is what we share in common with our fellow-men. It is knowledge about the Public World, the world of science, of social communication. Privacy is that body of statement which an individual makes when he expresses what he calls his own subjective experiences separated from the universe of discourse. It is essentially personal to himself. It cannot be directly shared with others, but presumably a poet or an artist may produce some public material that enables someone else to experience something correspondingly private. Science is thus a process, the process of building up the methodology of what he calls the Public World. In doing so he envisages the progressive extension of the Public World to include what lies at present within the realm of private beliefs. He sees in Pavlov's work a beginning of the undermining of purely subjective ideas of consciousness by separating out their public characteristics, and he recognises that one of the features of scientific advance has been the stripping from its explanations of all references to privacy. The study of the sense organs involves far-reaching consequences to science, in that man acquires his knowledge of the world through them. Thus the view of the universe constructed by the physical scientist is likely to be fundamentally altered by the further progress of Biology.

This must not be taken to imply, of course, that the evoking of some form of general assent is, of itself, a sufficient criterion for scientific truth, nor is it always a necessary one. As we shall see later, and as Hogben would agree, it has little relevance to the external relations of science, from which, as we shall also see, the internal relations cannot be neutrally isolated. All scientific discoveries are, in fact, not publicly verified. They may be capable of being so tested, but the experiment may not actually be repeated; and that for a very good reason. Moreover, it is not an exclusively scientific criterion. Science is not the only social activity that calls for such assent. Art no less than science requires some form of acceptance and recognition by others. It may be a very restricted public, but so also is the body of assessors of a new discovery in some abstruse branch of mathematics. Those who have had experience of the work of learned societies know quite well how difficult it is in many cases to find a referee adequately qualified to estimate the accuracy and truth of some pieces of work that are submitted. It is not that it is impossible to find someone capable of following the tortuous train of thought and action involved, but simply that the size of the public suitably equipped at any moment is exceedingly small. Art is in a similar case. Being social activities, both alike require to win acceptance in this sense before they can be accepted within the body of artistic or scientific expression. An important distinction between Science and Art resides in this, that whereas a work of art is accepted as a completed piece, a picture, a poem, a novel, the process that led up to its production plays no essential part in winning that acceptance. That is regarded as a *mere* matter of technique, although it may be very individual. With a scientific discovery it is rather different. Whatever be the urge that appears to spur the individual scientist to investigate a particular problem or to envisage the problem in a particular way, what is ultimately significant for science, in the present restricted sense, is the result *and* the process of arriving at it. A simple statement that there are scarlet elephants at the back of the moon would never win acceptance without a careful exposition of how this amazing conclusion was reached. The process might be too complex for all but the select few to follow, but the process would require to be stated. The method of acquiring the result, in fact, is as much part of the discovery as the so-called discovery itself, and it is in this wide sense that the criterion of *general assent* has to be understood. In art the act of acceptance appears to be direct. Art speaks from individual to individual, or from the individual to the social group. The route towards perception is not explicitly part of the artist's finished piece, although somehow or other it must be implicit in it, otherwise contact would be impossible. It is for that reason that art comes as a sudden personal revelation, science as a climax to cumulative evidence.

If the differences in behaviour of Scientists and Artists as classes are to be used as criteria in their respective domains, the distinction shows itself more obviously with regard to rejection than with regard to acceptance. A piece of scientific work definitely rejected by the experts in that field is rejected by the movement. The others assent to the rejection. In Art it is different. A piece of Sculpture may be rejected as hideous, featureless, and purposeless by one school and acclaimed as the work of a creative genius by another. In Science the criterion is more social than individual. The world of Art is not so consciously united.

In the last analysis, there is little difference between the *individual* effort of the artist and the scientist in the direct handling of his problem. Both exhibit intuition, inspiration, describe it how you will, in seeking the direction in which to find their immediate personal satisfaction. There is no clearly defined highway to produce even the most trivial work of science, just as there is no certain pathway to creative artistic work. Even in the discovery of a mathematical truth, however rigorous the logical system within which it will eventually require to be fitted, the objective is rarely if ever attained by a hard and fast sequence of premiss and deduction. The mind of the worker leaps forward, springing to conclusions long before they are established, beckoning ahead of the logic. It is a continuous process of exploration, of prospecting, at times systematic, at times merely groping. It is a game of trial and error, of hit and miss, but the proof that the shot is home awaits the ultimate arrival of the appropriate criteria. This is not to suggest that there is anything mystical in the process, but that it is a rather special feature of such thought activity. With the experimenter it is particularly pronounced. Before he decides the detailed nature of his test or the ensemble of his apparatus, he has already jumped ahead of his evidence and seeks the *expected* result. Verification drags slowly behind. He who is totally devoid of imagination can be neither scientist nor artist. Both, as individuals, seek the satisfaction of a personal urge, a need, and each in his own way produces his work of art. Viewed as a *personal* activity there is a close similarity in action.

A work of science, then, must provide a conclusion *and* a path, and all who can traverse the path can achieve the awaited conviction. Nevertheless that is not necessarily the first criterion that is applied. Because it is consistent with an expanding body of knowledge, because it clearly represents an accretion to a continuous movement, it may be accepted provisionally without that explicit verification upon which scientists pride themselves. This has, in fact, grown up as an unconscious tradition among scientists which acts almost as a social criterion of scientific good form. Mistakes are therefore inevitable. The history of science is peppered with refusals to face the truth, and later with admissions of false judgments. The path is a difficult and specialised one which few can tread, and the great majority of scientists are in reality novices in the face of all scientific work except their own restricted field. At the end of 1811, for example, Fourier submitted his now classic memoir to the Paris Academy on the *Propagation of Heat*. His adjudicators, Laplace, Lagrange, and Legendre, greatest triad of mathematicians of almost any single period, criticised the paper so severely that it was not published by the Academy. As secretary of that institution thirteen years later, Fourier published his results, now become a classic, in the *Mémoires*, without alteration from the original form. By that gesture he exposed to history the fallibility of scientific criteria and the force of continuity in the scientific movement as a factor in acceptance. " Even Cambridge mathematicians deserve justice," wrote Oliver Heaviside bitterly, when his profoundly important contributions to Mathematical Physics had been ignored for twenty-five years because his methods lacked the logical rigour the movement had bowed down to worship.

The great danger in endeavouring to discover what are the nature of the criteria that science demands for acceptance lies in the fact that one is inclined to generalise from the behaviour of the few. The movement is not a form of generalised behaviour. There is no average scientist who embodies within his conduct, as properties, the characteristics of the mass. Individuals differ in their outlook, but in the main they conform to the requirements of the herd, and the most significant criterion that is in fact applied to decide whether or not a new extension is to be accepted, lies in the answer to a query that is primarily social, rather than specifically scientific. Is it in the direct line of development of scientific knowledge? Other criteria of the type we have discussed enter with greater or less urgency after the answer to this has been found, but the tradition of knowledge and the inertia of method are factors of first importance. For no scientific man can stand alone. The problems with which he is concerned are not personal. They neither relate to him as an individual, nor are they of interest to him alone. Every upward thrust in knowledge is made from the scaffolding erected by the movement to which innumerable others have contributed. Where discoveries have been unjustly refused recognition in the past, as in the case of Fourier, Heaviside, Waterston, Mendel, to mention only a few outstanding names, it has invariably been due to the fact that their advances broke away too drastically from the track of the scientific herd. They were men with a flash of genius.

§ 5.

When the attempt is made to examine the criteria of science without recognising that it is essentially a social outgrowth, regarding it atomistically as a mere summation of interests of isolated individuals, it is not unnatural to find that the personal motives and urges of the constituent units are absorbed into the general scheme as if they played the predominant rôle. It is in effect yet another manifestation of the prevailing tendency to introduce idealist concepts into scientific exposition. This is well illustrated by the manner in which the so-called *simplicity factor* is presumed to operate in the selection and in the determination of scientific laws. *Simplicity* has been dealt with by writers from various angles, but it is worth while seeing in the first place how it appears to arise within scientific theory.

Is there more than one possible system of scientific laws consistent with the known facts of the universe and capable equally of fulfilling all the demands that science makes upon them? The prime requirement of a scientific law, as we have seen, is that it shall be valid for purposes of prediction. Has science at various stages in its history been faced with a choice of laws that equally well satisfy these requirements? Has a definite selection actually been made so that what science presents finally is only one of a possible series of scientific explanations or formulations? If such a choice is, in fact, presented and made, what criterion is it that guides the choice? Numerous writers—Sir A. Eddington, Sir J. Jeans, Dr. H. Jeffreys, J. W. N. Sullivan among others —all insist that in the last resort the criterion is of a purely personal nature. It is an appeal to simplicity. " Of two explanations, choose the simpler," it is suggested is a working principle in scientific procedure. With the exception of Jeffreys, none of these writers as far as I can find, attempts to give a scientific statement of what is implied by simplicity. The word is merely taken as it stands in common speech, with the implication that its use in the selection of alternative scientific laws is immediately apparent to all. More than this, it is presumed, although it is never mentioned, that all scientists faced with the same choice will agree at once which is the simplest law for the purposes in hand. An illustration frequently produced is taken from contemporary scientific theory. Both Einstein and Eddington have each offered an extension of the Relativity scheme for the unification of gravitational and electrical phenomena. Here were two formulations both fitting the known facts equally well. There was at that stage no experimental test to enable a discrimination to be made. You could take your choice of the simpler. Curiously enough, however, to each of the inventors his own formulation was the most commendable. There is here no agreement about a working principle, and consequently in the very circumstances in which we might have supposed it would operate successfully, the criterion fails.

Simplicity is apparently a difficult criterion to apply.

If those who advance such schemes of co-ordination cannot themselves agree, what do scientists as a class do in these circumstances? Is the simplicity criterion so definite in its operation as a socially scientific characteristic that they, apart from the inventors, unerringly and unanimously select one in preference to the other? The answer is, of course, in the negative. Both explanations are adopted tentatively until further experimental evidence may enable a distinction to be drawn. The ultimate criterion would seem, then, to be empiric, as indeed it has been in the case cited. Facts, not feelings, must speak. No doubt individual investigators will be drawn to that which appears simpler or more intriguing to them in order to work out its possible implications, but that is a very different matter from asserting that the, to him, simpler one is incorporated within the body of scientific theory. Jeffreys (*Scientific Inference*), approaching the question from the point of view of the individual scientist, implies, however, that the latter's actions and choice are typical of science as a whole, and therefore actually illustrate the operation of the criterion. His conclusion is that the simpler law is more probably true, and he seems to derive some satisfaction from the alleged fact that scientific workers in practice behave as if they believed this to be so.

Actually the so-called *simple* law is used to discover what isolated system, if any, may be found to fit it. It is an illustration of how mathematics may be used as a probe in the discovery of isolates. The conditions of the experiment are not initially defined as in this illustration. It is only in pure mathematics that one begins with such definitions, and from such definitions deductions are made. A genuine experiment involves an induction.

There is no such thing as a simple law, an absolute, the truth of which exists of its own right once one has *defined* the experiment. It is true that one may hit upon a simple formula, and use it to test whether a slight alteration of the experiment and its circumstances may not succeed in finding an experimental isolate, that will give this simple law. In this sense one cannot therefore talk of the truth of a scientific law, but rather of its range of validity. This implies an extent and a limit to its applicability, and that extent and that limit have to be found from an examination, not merely of the isolated experiment " defined " for us, but from the whole mass of similar scientific experiments that would seem to offer isolations of a similar type.

Truth is a dangerous word to incorporate within the vocabulary of science. It drags with it, in its train, ideas of permanence and immutability that are foreign to the spirit of a study that is essentially an historically changing movement, and that relies so much on practical examination within restricted circumstances. If it is true to say that the universe is for ever changing, that a situation once gone never recurs, then it is stupid to refer to the Laws of Science, based on such simple permanencies as measuring rods and clocks, as if each could equally well embody Truth. Truth is an absolute notion that science, which is not concerned with any such permanency, had better leave alone. The function of science is to find the scope of the environment, the isolate, that will make a stated law applicable. Alternatively it is to frame a statement that will be applicable to an apparently circumscribed environment. The function of science is, in fact, to make an appropriate adjustment between the two, for at no stage are either the details of the relevant environment explicitly known, nor is there a final form of the statement. We cannot merely say, Let us compress a gas and discover the law that relates pressure to volume. In doing so we will discover that there is no simple law worth having at that stage unless the experiment is circumscribed in a variety of ways. If we exclude changes in temperature, if the gas is not compressed too highly, nor the steady temperature maintained too low, and if a variety of other factors are carefully checked, then we have a set of circumstances that conform to the simple law discovered by Boyle. The hint that there might be a simple law has suggested seeking the environment of the experiment that made it applicable. If we are talking of real gases, then it would be merely stupid to say that they obey the law that pressure is inversely proportional to volume. It is too bald, too isolated a statement. It has to be related to the circumstances within which it has a valid application. They are not separately to be isolated. We see, then, that to deal with the set of experimental results as a set of numbers, dissociated not merely from the details of the experiment to which they refer, but from the whole matrix of scientific knowledge into which it must fit, is to commit a fallacious isolation. It ignores the fact that science is not a series of individual sporadic jumps, but a combined forward movement. Its laws grow out of the practice of the past and are tested and transformed at the bar of future practice.

The discussion of the place of truth in science has weakened if not destroyed the case for attaching any permanent weight to the statement that the simplest law is most probably the true law. For this implies a mathematical censorship of scientific experiment. It assumes that the experiment and its environment are postulated in advance, that the measurements are precisely given, and that all that has to be done is to find the simplest mathematical expression to fit these numbers. In just this way does one define in advance the mathematical concepts one proposes to discuss. In the world of experimental science, objects are not defined into existence. They have to be isolated and studied, and the result of that study provides information concerning what was " given." All that is, in fact, given in advance is the state of scientific knowledge of the period and the general lay-out and object of the experiment. Even these are themselves changed as the experiment proceeds. It is as much a study of these in relation to previous knowledge and a proposed " law " as it is a study of a law. In what way, then, if at all, does simplicity actually show itself in science? It becomes apparent in the way which one would expect if one remembers that science is a human effort restricted to adjust its conclusions to a world that is not only difficult to analyse, but even elusive to grasp because of its fleeting nature.

An individual scientist has all sorts of personal

choices about which he may please himself. He may choose the type of problem he proposes to study, but he does so from among a set restricted for him by the state of knowledge at the time. He may please himself how he will express his results, but they must be represented in a form continuous with those of other workers. He may represent them in mathematically simple or in complex form, but his individual feelings and choices in this respect are of little consequence in the general scientific trend. The form of the law that is finally adopted does not depend on any one set of experiments and on nothing else. The scientific scheme hangs together. If it did not smooth out individual preferences in this way, it would not be a unity, and it would not be science.

The scientific movement does not seize on every isolate it can imagine, to study the range of its neutrality. It chooses, as far as possible, the easiest route across a difficult region, and it does so by seeking the simplest isolates in the first instance. But a simple isolate that is fruitful in science must be simple not merely in statement, but, most important of all, in its experimental requirements, and in the light of the existing technique of the science. It follows that if an experiment suggests two or more possible laws the scientist will naturally explore that one which fulfils these simpler considerations. It is not that one is truth and the other falsehood. It is that the circumstances that have to be associated with the one to render it a continuous extension of previous knowledge, to make it applicable to all the known circumstances, are simpler than the other.

This is a point of some possible importance in relation to the content of science rather than to its truth. It implies that the picture of scientific knowledge that may be spread before us at any time in history, as far as its content is concerned, is affected to an extent we cannot estimate by the dictates of simplicity. But its significance can be over-stressed. Simplicity is not a constant factor. It continually emerges from complexity. It is a historically changing concept. To scientists of the Newtonian period the problems of electro-magnetism were insuperable. The forward march of science and technology had to pass through the age of Faraday and Maxwell. The complex problems of planetary motions that baffled Newton's predecessors are now a commonplace to every first- and second-year student of mathematics and physics. And so the movement in its advance tends to obliterate, by the tread of its many feet, whatever traces may have been left of its early simplicity.

§ 6.

The ranges of experiment and theory overlap, but they do not coincide. Theory builds on experiment, but it builds outwards, even at the limiting regions where our powers of observation fail, at the sub-atomic and at the ultra-astronomic extremes. With the breakdown in experimentation emerges also human and therefore scientific uncertainty, for in the last resort science can do no more than handle the limited material it can collect.

Historically the range of perception, the field from which it has been able to cull its raw material, has expanded steadily as science itself has expanded. The history of scientific instruments and scientific machinery is in this sense the history of continually extending claims that have swept in new regions for cultivation. But human beings are tied to the Earth; there is a limit to stellar space and the objects in it whose effects, even on our most delicate instruments, are perceptible. We can have knowledge only of what enters into our perceptual field, and much of that is inferred. What occurs outside can be a mere matter of conjecture. Precisely the same considerations apply to the minute fields of sub-atomic matter. What happens below a certain range of fineness we can only guess.

At such a level any two proposed schemes of activity that account for what is actually perceived are, therefore, equally tenable, and, provided they account for all the observed facts, are equally valid. Action only in these regions could undermine the description, and, they are beyond action. They must rank as mere theories, and, in so far as our scientific knowledge has enabled us to recognise the existence of a limit to the perceivable field, they must always remain theories. They cannot rank in this sense equally with the other scientific facts or generalisations that are continually capable of test and verification. When such a situation arises, as has recently arisen in the sub-microscopic and macroscopic regions of space, the selection of an explanation by a particular scientist becomes a mere matter of æsthetic choice, simplicity, or beauty, just as he prefers. It is a choice by the individual, and by its very nature scarcely affects the general movement that is science. To some extent this is the case with much that passes for " knowledge " concerning the nature of space. We do not seek an answer to the question " What is space? " Space itself is not a pure entity of this nature. It is an inferred isolate which we take as containing the physical world and within which the changing world processes occur. It is like the sheet of paper on which we propose to draw a map, and for that purpose we choose the kind of map projection that suits us best. In that sense it is an instrument. It may be on a flat sheet or on the surface of a globe. The choice that is made is dictated by two considerations. In the first place, it has to be such as enables our widely extended knowledge of the universe, our scientific knowledge, to be fully mapped out. In the second place, it must be such that the mapping system that is selected must also fit the limited world of common-sense experience. Common-sense experience does not extend to the outer nebulæ, nor would it be common sense if its simple inferences were assumed to be applicable there. It is restricted to within a comparatively short distance of space or time. It follows, therefore, that the nature of the space that is selected for this scientific, but largely mathematical, mapping may appear strange to the uninitiated, but no stranger than any other abstruse mathematical formula would appear. To the scientist the important point is that it appears to enable the facts that are known to be fitted together and to provide a means of prediction, that most crucial test of scientific utility. The facts are not many at such extreme regions of observation, but they have most stubbornly resisted reconciliation with all previous theories.

An illustration of how such explanations have been achieved may be seen in what has become known as the " expanding universe." Einstein's modified Law of Gravitation, derived on the basis of his extended scheme of mapping that we call four-dimensional space, has shown that, in addition to the ordinary attraction that was announced by Newton, isolated bodies must have the " property " of repelling each other. While the attractive force diminishes as the distances between bodies increase, the simultaneous repellent force increases. At enormous distances apart, where the attractive forces are weak, bodies will be urged still further apart. This would follow from Einstein's Law as a deduction from the nature of the " Space " upon which he chose to map the major features of the physical world on a grand scale. Recently measurements have been taken of the motion of those island universes we call nebulæ, vast collections of stars and universes like our own. Of ninety such nebulæ whose speeds have been measured it appears that eighty-seven are receding from each other and from us. The others are sufficiently near to make it possible that the ordinary gravitational attractions balance the repellent effects. Their movement is not great. Thus the observations themselves, apart from any direct gravitational theory, suggest that the whole universe is expanding, but the significant feature from the point of scientific theory is that here, at any rate, is a prediction. Nevertheless, so meagre are the means at our disposal for verifying such theories at their crucial points in sufficient detail or for testing them in action, that they must remain mere theories at the outer fringes of scientific knowledge. They are not inconsistent with the general trend of the movement in scientific knowledge, but they must not be translated into the experience of simple common sense. They are the parts of an extended mathematical framework, tested only at isolated places.

§ 7.

Science as it is understood by its devotees is concerned with what we have called its internal relations only. Even an examination of these has brought us continually to the same point, that what is primarily significant at any level is the relation to the larger movement. The individual contribution of the scientist must fit into the field of knowledge and experience as it has emerged to that stage. He breaks away at his peril. The criteria of acceptance have a strong sociological flavour. Just as it is from matter that the atom or the electron has to be isolated, so it is the scientific movement that makes

the individual scientist, and society that makes
science possible. The idealist doctrines that at
present dominate scientific philosophy are an
attempt to invert the procedure, regarding the individual as the pinnacle upon which the universe has
to be poised, conceiving of the atomistic approach
as affording the basic explanation of matter in the
mass, conceiving of individuals as isolated entities
pursuing isolated experiments and constructing laws
that depend on individual preference, and so constructing science. In just this way scientists tend
to isolate their movement as if it were an end in
itself, and, pursuing "Science for its own sake,"
ignore the social implications of their work.

The keynote of scientific method, as we have
seen, is the search for systems capable of being
neutrally isolated. This procedure is forced upon
science if it is to handle any part of the vast complex
of material and activity that is the process of Nature.
In taking this step the scientist is introducing a
barrier, an artificial barrier between diverse aspects
of the same phenomena. For example, it induces
him to separate off a human being from his social
surroundings and his æsthetic tastes, as a mere
mass of blood, bones, and breathing apparatus. It
enables him to isolate for study the chemical
attributes of tri-nitro-toluol as an explosive sub-

stance irrespective of what functions it may fulfil in the next war. He is thereby placed in the position of examining groups of events as apparently self-contained islands without requiring to concern himself unduly, or at all, with other connections that his material necessarily has with the changing world. Rigorously speaking the statements science makes concerning its isolates must not be taken to represent all that is significant about that material. They can at best be aspects, mere elements broken off from the whole, with a status similar to that of an amputated limb. The lessons of science cannot be read aright unless the material with which it is concerned is examined in a much wider setting than that of the mere scientific isolate. Science has to allow for the significant part of the environment that is ignored in setting up the isolate, by fixing *properties* to it, but what is significant for the scientist does not necessarily cover all that is otherwise of importance. Natural science covers merely what we have called the internal aspects. Thus the study of the speeds at which a rotating shaft will fly to pieces, or the length of time insensibility will last after one inhales a given quantity of nitrous oxide, are problems concerning the internal relations of the sub-isolates of these systems, the shaft and its rotation, the human body and the drug. For the study of these internal relations evidence is demanded that turns out to be acceptable to individuals of every creed or colour, class, or race. These internal isolates are neutral and impersonal.

The interest in a steel shaft does not finish with its internal isolates, with the characteristics that natural science separates off for its convenience. A shaft has other functions, operates in other environments that justify us in attaching yet further properties to it. It may, for example, be part of a turbine, which functions in the world of production and transport. The shaft has therefore social properties, because it is a social instrument. It is an isolate within the environment of society, and it has largely been because of the study of the scientific characteristics of such things as shafts that it has been transformed into such a *useful* weapon in production.

While for some purposes, we may treat the partial scientific characteristics of such an isolate and neglect its social aspect, the two are in reality intimately bound up in it. What is the social function of the shaft or the turbine? is a vital question which remains. In what way does it operate in production? Which individual, which class, which nation, which race will it serve? These and other questions arise at once as soon as we recognise that the social functions of the turbine are significant attributes of it. Since the very effectiveness of the object on the social side rests on the success that has been attained when dealing with the purely scientific aspects, since, in fact, it is through science that the instruments of production and of destruction are sharpened, science shows itself not as a movement capable of being permanently isolated as neutral from the rest of changing society, but as a definite instrument serving the ends for which production is carried out. If the scientific movement is to be appreciated for what it is, it is essential that its isolates, artificially introduced to allow of neutral study, must be ultimately removed. The scientist cannot be said to have appreciated the significance of his work unless he has undertaken this task.

An important distinction can now be drawn between what we have called the internal isolates, those with which science is concerned in the restricted sense, and the external isolates, those with which the scientific movement is concerned in its social relationships. The criteria for the former, if they could be rigorously applied, are impersonal, they are neutral to individual valuations, and therefore in a very individual sense may be regarded as ethically neutral. Since, however, no piece of scientific work, when we include its external relations, can really be divorced from the social function to which it contributes, science can be no more ethically neutral than the purposes for which production is undertaken. The ethical setting of the scientific movement is scarcely apparent to scientific workers engaged on more purely theoretical problems, but it becomes increasingly insistent as applied science and technology is approached, applied as it must be to social ends. The distinction can perhaps be seen in this way. Christian, Atheist, Jew, Socialist, Capitalist, and Anarchist alike will all agree that the number of words on this page is 218. All measurement, no matter how involved, falls into this category if we artificially suppose the process to stop there. But measurement is a means to a further end. Thus if we turn to a branch of applied science—applied, that is to say, to social purposes—the situation is completely different. In various branches of engineering, for example, there are always certain Factors of Safety—in reality factors of ignorance. It may be possible to estimate the stresses that will be set up in the structural parts of an aeroplane during flight, but there are always present certain unknown factors, certain weaknesses that may involve serious consequences in case of emergency. To allow for these contingencies, individual portions of the structure are usually made much stronger than the calculations suggest. This constitutes the factor of safety, but it involves also extra expenditure on material in the production, and possibly in the end greater cost, for in fact the safety factor may actually be larger than is really required. Similar considerations apply to practically every engineering structure, and, be it noted, such structures are invariably in use in social production or for other social purposes. A mine accident, a railway disaster, or a factory explosion occurs, and some experts will demonstrate that as far as the owners were concerned all reasonable safeguards had been taken, while others will show that the factor of safety was too low for the workers' well-being. In practice the experts themselves disagree. From the contrasting points of view of the owners and of the men the machinery fulfils two totally different functions. Immediately the social purpose of a piece of scientific work becomes apparent its ethical or social neutrality vanishes.

The line of ethical demarcation between pure and applied science cannot be maintained. It is ultimately an artificial distinction. The scientific movement is an integrated whole, and no advance, however trivial, however theoretical, can be isolated completely from the general movement of which it partakes. In so far as the products of science are misused, the responsibility of at least protesting lies on the shoulders of every individual scientist. It is a responsibility that also rests on the movement. It cannot be avoided by shutting tight the study doors to worship in silence—" Science for its own Sake "—as an Absolute Principle of Isolation.

INDEX